Enjoy

The Homekeeper's Diary 2022

FRANCIS BRENNAN

Gill Books

Gill Books
Hume Avenue
Park West
Dublin 12
www.gillbooks.ie

Gill Books is an imprint of
M.H. Gill and Co.

© Francis Brennan 2021

978 07171 9139 0

Edited by Alison Walsh
Proofread by Susan McKeever
Portrait photography by Barry Murphy
Styling by Ann Marie O'Leary
Designed by iota (www.iota-books.ie)
This book is typeset in Hoefler, DIN
    and Brandon Grotesque
Printed by L.E.G.O. SpA, Italy

© 'I am Kerry', The Estate of Sigerson Clifford, 1986.
Reprinted by kind permission of Mercier Press, Cork.

For permission to reproduce photographs, the
author and publisher gratefully acknowledge the
following: © Barry Murphy: 18, 21, 44, 88, 112, 118,
148, 158, 172; © iStock/Getty Premium: 27, 36, 39,
70, 74, 80, 94, 100, 106, 126, 134, 142, 152, 164, 176;
© Shutterstock: 19.

A CIP catalogue record for this book is available
from the British Library.
5 4 3 2 1

Name:

Address:

Eircode:

Phone number:

Email address:

Emergency contacts: 1.

2.

About the Author

Francis Brennan is the bestselling author of *It's the Little Things*, *Counting My Blessings*, *Francis Brennan's Book of Household Management* and *A Gentleman Abroad*. He presents one of Ireland's most popular TV shows, *At Your Service*. Together with his brother John he is co-owner of the five-star Park Hotel Kenmare and The Lansdowne Kenmare.

CONTENTS

A NOTE FROM FRANCIS

When I wrote last year's little note to you all, little did I imagine what we'd all go through in the following months. It seemed as if the world was turned upside down overnight. Working in the hospitality business as we do, John and I spent most of those months worrying and hoping and keeping our spirits up, wondering when we'd be welcoming guests to the Park Hotel Kenmare once more. The one thing that kept us going was the knowledge that we weren't alone. So many of you had similar stories to tell, of bereavement, of jobs lost, of illness, of loneliness and isolation, but also of extraordinary grit and determination. I was lost in admiration for the many people out there who turned their bad luck into opportunity, from publicans to retailers, to artists, actors, musicians and so on. I was so touched by all of those stories, from the retailers who took to doing house calls – socially distanced, of course! – to their valued customers, to the restaurants who turned themselves into takeaways or meal-kit makers, or coffee shops. The publicans who turned their pub into a local hub, or, in one case, a wildlife hospital; the stories of people's resilience and strength and their willingness to help others gave me hope and the courage to forge ahead and to look forward to better days.

I doubt any of us will forget the past couple of years, nor the lessons we learned about what really matters. I, for one, have learned to be grateful not just for our fantastic medical community, but also for the little acts of kindness I received every day from local people and the support John and I got from Irish visitors when we were able to open the hotel. We made new friends whom I hope will visit us many times in the future. I've also learned to appreciate the simple things that make my day a bit brighter: a nice, hot cup of tea and a slice of homemade cake, a sunny morning, a chat and a laugh with friends, even if it is on Zoom!

As I write, I'm in Kerry and it's springtime and after the long, cold winter, the sun is out and the daffodils are in bloom. This reminds me that no matter what, the seasons still come and go and things can and do get better. I wish you all a happy and healthy 2022.

ESSENTIAL INFORMATION

Health

Doctor	
Dentist	
Health insurance policy number	
PPS number	
Children's PPS numbers	
Name	Number
Name	Number
Name	Number
Name	Number
Local hospital	
Blood group	
Dentist	
Physiotherapist	
EHIC number	expires
Vet	
Pet insurance policy number	

Money

Bank	
Credit union	
Post office	
Credit card helpline	
Overseas credit card helpline	

Around the house

Hairdresser	
Plumber	
Electrician	
Gas company	
Oil supplier	
Nearest Garda station	
Home insurance provider	
Home insurance policy number	

Children

Childminder	
School office	
Children's phone numbers	
Name	Number
Name	Number
Name	Number
Name	Number

Cars

Car registration number		
Breakdown assistance		
Car insurance provider		
Car insurance policy number		
Mechanic		
Nearest NCT testing centre		Test due
Car tax renewal		
Local taxi service		

Work

Office	
Direct line	

Useful websites and numbers

National Car Testing Service	www.ncts.ie	
Department of Foreign Affairs	www.dfa.ie/passportonline/	
Citizens Information	www.citizensinformation.ie	076 107 4000
Irish Rail	www.irishrail.ie	1850 366 222
Bus Éireann	www.buseireann.ie	1850 836 611
Translink NI Railways/Translink Ulsterbus	www.translink.co.uk	028 (048) 9066 6630
Dublin Bus	www.dublinbus.ie	01 873 4222

2022 AT A GLANCE

JANUARY
M	T	W	T	F	S	S
					1	2
3	4	5	6	7	8	9
10	11	12	13	14	15	16
17	18	19	20	21	22	23
24	25	26	27	28	29	30
31						

FEBRUARY
M	T	W	T	F	S	S
	1	2	3	4	5	6
7	8	9	10	11	12	13
14	15	16	17	18	19	20
21	22	23	24	25	26	27
28						

MARCH
M	T	W	T	F	S	S
	1	2	3	4	5	6
7	8	9	10	11	12	13
14	15	16	17	18	19	20
21	22	23	24	25	26	27
28	29	30	31			

APRIL
M	T	W	T	F	S	S
				1	2	3
4	5	6	7	8	9	10
11	12	13	14	15	16	17
18	19	20	21	22	23	24
25	26	27	28	29	30	

MAY
M	T	W	T	F	S	S
						1
2	3	4	5	6	7	8
9	10	11	12	13	14	15
16	17	18	19	20	21	22
23	24	25	26	27	28	29
30	31					

JUNE
M	T	W	T	F	S	S
		1	2	3	4	5
6	7	8	9	10	11	12
13	14	15	16	17	18	19
20	21	22	23	24	25	26
27	28	29	30			

JULY
M	T	W	T	F	S	S
				1	2	3
4	5	6	7	8	9	10
11	12	13	14	15	16	17
18	19	20	21	22	23	24
25	26	27	28	29	30	31

AUGUST
M	T	W	T	F	S	S
1	2	3	4	5	6	7
8	9	10	11	12	13	14
15	16	17	18	19	20	21
22	23	24	25	26	27	28
29	30	31				

SEPTEMBER
M	T	W	T	F	S	S
			1	2	3	4
5	6	7	8	9	10	11
12	13	14	15	16	17	18
19	20	21	22	23	24	25
26	27	28	29	30		

OCTOBER
M	T	W	T	F	S	S
					1	2
3	4	5	6	7	8	9
10	11	12	13	14	15	16
17	18	19	20	21	22	23
24	25	26	27	28	29	30
31						

NOVEMBER
M	T	W	T	F	S	S
	1	2	3	4	5	6
7	8	9	10	11	12	13
14	15	16	17	18	19	20
21	22	23	24	25	26	27
28	29	30				

DECEMBER
M	T	W	T	F	S	S
			1	2	3	4
5	6	7	8	9	10	11
12	13	14	15	16	17	18
19	20	21	22	23	24	25
26	27	28	29	30	31	

Bank and public holidays in Ireland 2022

Saturday 1 January – New Year's Day

Thursday 17 March – St Patrick's Day

Friday 15 April – Good Friday

Sunday 17 April – Easter Sunday

Monday 18 April – Easter Monday

Monday 2 May – May bank holiday

Monday 6 June – June bank holiday

Monday 1 August – August bank holiday

Monday 31 October – October bank holiday

Sunday 25 December – Christmas Day

Monday 26 December – St Stephen's Day

2023

JANUARY
M	T	W	T	F	S	S
						1
2	3	4	5	6	7	8
9	10	11	12	13	14	15
16	17	18	19	20	21	22
23	24	25	26	27	28	29
30	31					

FEBRUARY
M	T	W	T	F	S	S
		1	2	3	4	5
6	7	8	9	10	11	12
13	14	15	16	17	18	19
20	21	22	23	24	25	26
27	28					

MARCH
M	T	W	T	F	S	S
		1	2	3	4	5
6	7	8	9	10	11	12
13	14	15	16	17	18	19
20	21	22	23	24	25	26
27	28	29	30	31		

APRIL
M	T	W	T	F	S	S
					1	2
3	4	5	6	7	8	9
10	11	12	13	14	15	16
17	18	19	20	21	22	23
24	25	26	27	28	29	30

MAY
M	T	W	T	F	S	S
1	2	3	4	5	6	7
8	9	10	11	12	13	14
15	16	17	18	19	20	21
22	23	24	25	26	27	28
29	30	31				

JUNE
M	T	W	T	F	S	S
			1	2	3	4
5	6	7	8	9	10	11
12	13	14	15	16	17	18
19	20	21	22	23	24	25
26	27	28	29	30		

JULY
M	T	W	T	F	S	S
					1	2
3	4	5	6	7	8	9
10	11	12	13	14	15	16
17	18	19	20	21	22	23
24	25	26	27	28	29	30
31						

AUGUST
M	T	W	T	F	S	S
	1	2	3	4	5	6
7	8	9	10	11	12	13
14	15	16	17	18	19	20
21	22	23	24	25	26	27
28	29	30	31			

SEPTEMBER
M	T	W	T	F	S	S
				1	2	3
4	5	6	7	8	9	10
11	12	13	14	15	16	17
18	19	20	21	22	23	24
25	26	27	28	29	30	

OCTOBER
M	T	W	T	F	S	S
						1
2	3	4	5	6	7	8
9	10	11	12	13	14	15
16	17	18	19	20	21	22
23	24	25	26	27	28	29
30	31					

NOVEMBER
M	T	W	T	F	S	S
		1	2	3	4	5
6	7	8	9	10	11	12
13	14	15	16	17	18	19
20	21	22	23	24	25	26
27	28	29	30			

DECEMBER
M	T	W	T	F	S	S
				1	2	3
4	5	6	7	8	9	10
11	12	13	14	15	16	17
18	19	20	21	22	23	24
25	26	27	28	29	30	31

2024

JANUARY
M	T	W	T	F	S	S
1	2	3	4	5	6	7
8	9	10	11	12	13	14
15	16	17	18	19	20	21
22	23	24	25	26	27	28
29	30	31				

FEBRUARY
M	T	W	T	F	S	S
			1	2	3	4
5	6	7	8	9	10	11
12	13	14	15	16	17	18
19	20	21	22	23	24	25
26	27	28	29			

MARCH
M	T	W	T	F	S	S
				1	2	3
4	5	6	7	8	9	10
11	12	13	14	15	16	17
18	19	20	21	22	23	24
25	26	27	28	29	30	31

APRIL
M	T	W	T	F	S	S
1	2	3	4	5	6	7
8	9	10	11	12	13	14
15	16	17	18	19	20	21
22	23	24	25	26	27	28
29	30					

MAY
M	T	W	T	F	S	S
		1	2	3	4	5
6	7	8	9	10	11	12
13	14	15	16	17	18	19
20	21	22	23	24	25	26
27	28	29	30	31		

JUNE
M	T	W	T	F	S	S
					1	2
3	4	5	6	7	8	9
10	11	12	13	14	15	16
17	18	19	20	21	22	23
24	25	26	27	28	29	30

JULY
M	T	W	T	F	S	S
1	2	3	4	5	6	7
8	9	10	11	12	13	14
15	16	17	18	19	20	21
22	23	24	25	26	27	28
29	30	31				

AUGUST
M	T	W	T	F	S	S
			1	2	3	4
5	6	7	8	9	10	11
12	13	14	15	16	17	18
19	20	21	22	23	24	25
26	27	28	29	30	31	

SEPTEMBER
M	T	W	T	F	S	S
						1
2	3	4	5	6	7	8
9	10	11	12	13	14	15
16	17	18	19	20	21	22
23	24	25	26	27	28	29
30						

OCTOBER
M	T	W	T	F	S	S
	1	2	3	4	5	6
7	8	9	10	11	12	13
14	15	16	17	18	19	20
21	22	23	24	25	26	27
28	29	30	31			

NOVEMBER
M	T	W	T	F	S	S
				1	2	3
4	5	6	7	8	9	10
11	12	13	14	15	16	17
18	19	20	21	22	23	24
25	26	27	28	29	30	

DECEMBER
M	T	W	T	F	S	S
						1
2	3	4	5	6	7	8
9	10	11	12	13	14	15
16	17	18	19	20	21	22
23	24	25	26	27	28	29
30	31					

Phases of the Moon

New Moon	First Quarter	Full Moon	Third Quarter
2 January	9 January	17 January	25 January
1 February	8 February	16 February	23 February
2 March	10 March	18 March	25 March
1 April	9 April	16 April	23 April
30 April	9 May	16 May	22 May
30 May	7 June	14 June	21 June
29 June	7 July	13 July	20 July
28 July	5 August	12 August	19 August
27 August	3 September	10 September	17 September
25 September	3 October	9 October	17 October
25 October	1 November	8 November	16 November
23 November	30 November	8 December	16 December
23 December	30 December		

Lunar events Ireland 2022

Solar Eclipse – 30 April
Total Lunar Eclipse – 16 May
Partial Solar Eclipse – 25 October
Total Lunar Eclipse – 8 November

Names for the Moon throughout the year

January – Wolf Moon
February – Snow Moon
March – Worm Moon
April – Pink Moon
May – Flower Moon
June – Strawberry Moon
July – Buck Moon
August – Sturgeon Moon
September – Harvest Moon
October – Hunter's Moon
November – Beaver Moon
December – Cold Moon

Sunrise and sunset times 2022

Dublin	Sunrise	Sunset
1 January 2022	08.40	16.17
1 February 2022	08.09	17.08
1 March 2022	07.12	18.02
1 April 2022	06.58	20.00
1 May 2022	05.51	20.54
1 June 2022	05.03	21.42
1 July 2022	05.01	21.56
1 August 2022	05.41	21.20
1 September 2022	06.34	20.14
1 October 2022	07.26	19.02
1 November 2022	07.23	16.52
1 December 2022	08.17	16.10

Cork	Sunrise	Sunset
1 January 2022	08.41	16.33
1 February 2022	08.13	17.22
1 March 2022	07.19	18.13
1 April 2022	07.09	20.07
1 May 2022	06.04	20.58
1 June 2022	05.20	21.43
1 July 2022	05.18	21.56
1 August 2022	05.56	21.23
1 September 2022	06.45	20.21
1 October 2022	07.34	19.11
1 November 2022	07.28	17.05
1 December 2022	08.18	16.26

Tides 2022

		1 Jan	1 Feb	1 Mar	1 Apr	1 May	1 Jun	1 Jul	1 Aug	1 Sep	1 Oct	1 Nov	1 Dec
Dublin	h/t	10:11 22:39	11:40	10:39 23:14	00:35 12:44	00:40 12:50	01:17 13:37	01:33 14:00	02:25 14:54	03:13 15:39	03:37 15:58	04:38 16:56	05:44 17:54
	l/t	03:23 15:50	04:53 17:23	03:56 16:25	06:00 18:24	06:10 18:29	07:00 19:13	07:23 19:31	08:15 20:20	09:00 21:12	09:20 21:46	10:18 23:15	11:17
Cork	h/t	03:40 16:08	05:18 17:41	04:20 16:43	06:27 18:45	06:34 18:50	07:16 19:34	07:34 19:55	08:27 20:47	09:12 21:34	09:32 21:56	10:26 23:04	11:29
	l/t	10:12 22:39	11:50	10:50 23:10	00:34 12:56	00:42 12:59	01:23 19:34	01:42 13:57	02:37 14:51	03:21 15:38	03:36 16:00	04:14 16:58	05:18 18:01
Belfast	h/t	09:30 21:56	10:59 23:32	09:57 22:33	12:05	00:05 12:15	00:47 13:07	01:02 13:29	01:53 14:23	02:43 15:11	03:08 15:31	04:05 16:22	05:08 17:16
	l/t	03:16 15:45	04:48 17:22	03:47 16:20	05:58 18:24	06:10 18:29	07:01 19:12	07:22 19:28	08:17 20:20	09:04 21:14	09:22 21:47	10:07 23:01	11:03 23:54
Galway	h/t	03:31 15:58	05:00 17:28	04:07 16:35	06:06 18:27	06:13 18:30	06:59 19:13	07:23 19:33	08:13 20:22	08:52 21:09	09:10 21:38	10:14 23:24	11:21
	l/t	09:36 21:56	11:06 23:22	10:13 22:29	12:06	12:10	00:42 12:53	01:04 13:14	01:54 14:03	02:32 14:49	02:48 15:15	03:47 16:46	04:59 17:45

CONVERSION TABLES

I used to go half mad trying to work out what US cups were in grams and so on, so this handy primer will come in useful for me as well as you! Also, www.onlineconversion.com allows you to convert any measurement.

 HEAT
°C x 1.8 + 32 = °F
°F − 32 / 1.8 = °C

 **VOLUME**

Gas	°F	°C
¼	250	120
1	275	140
2	300	150
3	325	170
4	350	180
5	375	190
6	400	200
7	425	220
8	450	230
9	475	240

One cup	Imperial	Metric
Caster sugar	8oz	225g
Brown sugar	6oz	170g
Butter	8oz	115g
Flour	5oz	140g
Raisins	7oz	200g
Syrup	12oz	340g

1 TEASPOON = 5ML
1 DESSERTSPOON = 10ML
1 TABLESPOON = 15ML

WEIGHT
1KG = 35OZ/2.2LB

 **LIQUIDS**

Imperial	Metric
½oz	15g
¾oz	20g
1oz	30g
2oz	60g
3oz	85g
4oz (¼lb)	115g
5oz	140g
6oz	170g
7oz	200g
8oz (½lb)	230g
9oz	255g
10oz	285g
11oz	310g
12oz (¾lb)	340g
13oz	370g
14oz	400g
15oz	425g
16oz (1lb)	450g
24oz	680g
32oz (2lb)	0.9kg
48oz (3lb)	1.4kg
64oz (4lb)	1.8kg

Pint	Metric	Cup	fl. oz
	100ml		3½
	125ml	½	4½
¼	150ml		5
	200ml		7
	250ml	1	9
½	275ml		10
	300ml		11
	400ml		14
	500ml	2	18
1	570ml		20
	750ml	3	26
1¾	1.0l	4	35

WASHING SYMBOLS

Last year, with no launderettes or dry cleaners open, I became an expert in the art of handwashing and fabric care. Here's a handy primer on the most common symbols.

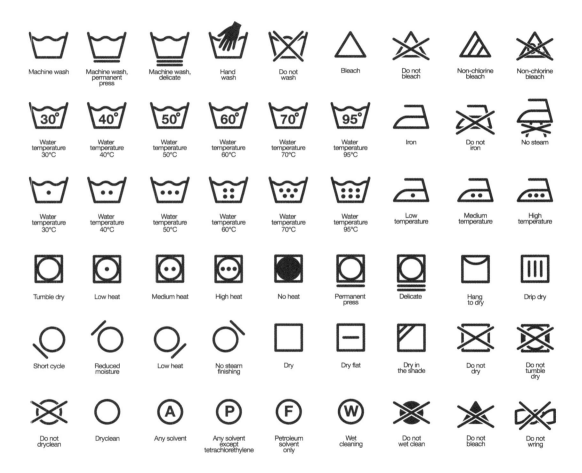

CARING FOR FABRICS

The other thing I learned last year – the hard way – was how to care for delicate fabrics. I had a couple of accidents with shrinking items of clothing, so now I'm careful to (a) check the label and (b) look up a 'how to' so my precious delicates don't end up a shrivelled mess. Here's a handy table of the most common fabrics and how to care for them.

WOOL	SILK	COTTON
Have you ever put a woollen jumper in the wash and taken it out to discover it's like a little ball of felt? I have. Wool should be washed in lukewarm water with a gentle detergent. Don't knead it vigorously or wring it out – a gentle squeeze is best, before shaping your damp woollen item and drying it flat. A friend of mine pops her jumpers in a colander and lets them drip away before doing this, which is very clever.	Again, lukewarm water is best, and a specialist detergent – but before you wash, do a patch test to check that your garment is colour-fast. Dampen a little corner of the item and press it into a white towel – if the colour comes off, you'll need to have it dry-cleaned.	I used to wash my cottons in a hot wash, before I discovered that not all cottons are the same. So my nice 100 per cent cotton shirt needs a cold wash, but my cotton bedsheets, underwear and bath towels need a hot one to get rid of any nasties. I also don't tumble dry cotton clothes, because they shrink, and I turn them inside out before washing to preserve them better.

LINEN	ATHLEISURE
I love linen, because it's a gorgeous fabric and it's not that hard to look after. Lukewarm water is your friend, along with a mild detergent. You can wash it in the machine (although I'd get linen jackets dry-cleaned because of their shape and because the lining might shrink) on a delicates setting. Dry your linens flat and iron while damp. Don't iron them when fully dry or you'll fix the creases.	Nowadays, so many of us wear this not only to the gym but also in everyday life. However, you don't need to wash it on a hot cycle to get rid of bacteria – if you do, the garments won't last. Cold water is your friend, and provided you wash your garments after exercise and reasonably frequently, germs should not be an issue. A pre-soak with half a cup of white vinegar in cold water will really help with odour. Don't use fabric softener on athleisure, because it damages the fibres, and don't dry-clean it. Instead, roll it in a towel to absorb moisture and then dry it flat.

FRANCIS'S HANDY HOW TO ...

Change a car tyre

1. Make sure that you are parked safely and on the level.
2. Put the car into first/reverse and put the handbrake on.
3. Find the spare tyre (mine is in a cage under the boot) and the jack, which should be close by in the car's toolkit (mine is in a unit at the edge of the boot). My car jack is a diamond-shaped one with a handle which I use to crank the jack up.
4. Place the jack underneath the car on the same side as your punctured tyre. Some cars have a little groove in the metal to show you where the jack should go. Otherwise, place it firmly under the metalwork.
5. Turn the jack until it is just resting against the metalwork above. You don't want to lift the car just yet.
6. Loosen the screws that hold the tyre in place. You'll have a cross wrench in your car toolkit. Place it over each bolt and turn anti-clockwise until the bolt loosens. You might need to loosen the bolts by giving the wrench a nudge with your foot.
7. Now twist the jack so that the car gradually rises. Make sure it's going up straight; if it isn't, readjust the jack.
8. Finish loosening the bolts and remove them. Pull the tyre out and put it to one side.
9. Put the spare tyre on – the right way round! – and turn the nuts clockwise to tighten them. Do this by hand, before using the wrench.
10. Lower the jack gently.
11. Tighten any nuts that need it, then put your tyre into the boot to remind you to take it to the garage.

Sew on a button

1. Get yourself one of those handy little sewing kits that come in a plastic box. They usually contain a row of threads in a few colours, a pair of nail scissors, a measuring tape, a few needles and pins and possibly one of those needle-threading gadgets – it's a small metallic plate with a wire loop attached, through which you push the thread into the needle.

2. Pick a thread in a colour as close as possible to the material onto which you are sewing the button.

3. Thread the needle. I turn my needle slightly side on, so that I can judge where the thread goes into the eye of the needle and pull it through – making sure that I'm wearing my reading glasses.

4. Pull through a good 20cm of thread – long enough to be able to go through the buttonholes a few times, but not so long that it gets tangled up in a big knot! If in doubt, pull your thread through and double it, so that the thread will be stronger.

5. Tie a knot in the end of your single or double thread: make a loop by wrapping the thread around your finger, push the end of the thread through, then pull the thread tight. This will stop your thread going straight through the material.

6. Lift the dress/shirt/coat towards you and find the place where the button was originally sewn on. Push the needle and thread through to the other side and then back – and then again – so you have a little mark to indicate where the button should go.

7. With one hand, place the button at the spot and hold with your thumb on the button and your finger underneath the fabric.

8. Take the needle and thread in your free hand and push it from underneath the fabric through one of the holes in the button, holding the button in place with a finger. Once the thread is through one hole, pop a pin into the gap between the button and the material, before pushing the needle back through the

opposite hole. This will stop you pulling the thread through so tightly that the fabric puckers.

9. Push the needle back into the opposite hole, through the fabric to the underside, pulling the thread fully through, then begin the process again. Do this until the button is securely sewn back on.

10. Remove the pin, then lift the button slightly and wrap your thread around the thread between the button and the fabric. Then push the needle back through the fabric to the underside and push the needle a few times through the little stitch you'll have created underneath. Finally, snip off the thread with the scissors.

Tidy up a trouser hem

1. Turn your trousers inside out and locate the loose hem.

2. Place the leg of the trousers on a flat surface and find where the loose thread of the hem is. Pin the little gap where the thread has come loose about halfway between the bottom and the top of the hem.

3. Thread your needle – you'll be an expert now! – and begin. Don't push your needle all of the way through, but simply 'pick up' a few threads.

4. Push your needle through the folded bit of the fabric, pulling from back to front – pick up a few threads from the fabric above the hem, before moving along a little bit and pushing the needle through the fold again – and repeat until the gap has been covered, before tying off.

5. As you pick up your threads, turn the leg inside out for a moment to check that the thread isn't showing on the outside, then continue.

Change a plug

1. Unscrew the centre screw on your plug with a Phillips head screwdriver.
2. Loosen the two screws at the bottom – the ones that hold the cable in place.
3. Remove the little clamp.
4. Check carefully which wires go into which terminal – before you loosen each terminal to remove the wires using a flat-head screwdriver. Green and yellow = earth; brown = live; blue = neutral.
5. Remove the wires and prepare the new plug by opening it in the same way as you opened the old one.
6. Prepare the wires for the new plug. You might need to strip some of the casing off the wires using pliers, but don't cut into the wires themselves. Arrange the wires in the correct positions for each terminal.
7. Snip a tiny bit off the wires so that you can see the copper, which you then twist before placing in each terminal. Again, make sure the correct wire is in the correct terminal!
8. Screw the terminals down onto the copper wire, then press the flex into the relevant slot – the flex, not the wires – before tightening the clamp, screwing it over the flex, then snapping both sides of the plug together and tightening the external screw.

Put up a shelf

I learned how to do this the hard way – by putting one up and seeing it fall down! Here's what I found out:

1. Assemble the tools you'll need for the job: a spirit level, drill, screws and a stud detector (sometimes this comes as part of a device that allows you to check for cables as well).

2. The stud detector will enable you to find the studs, which are the uprights behind the plasterboard. When you find them, mark them with your pencil from top to bottom. You'll be attaching your brackets to the studs.
3. Take one shelf bracket and place it against one set of lines marking the stud. Use the spirit level (held vertically) to check that it's straight. Make sure that you aren't leaning to one side when you're using your spirit level.
4. Mark through the screw holes in the bracket with a pencil.
5. Take your drill and attach the right drill bit. It should be slightly smaller than your screws, so that they stay put when you screw them in.
6. Find a screw of the correct length. Depending on the thickness of your plasterboard, your screws should be long enough to go through the plasterboard and the stud – line them up against your drill bit to compare the two.
7. Drill the holes for your screws where you made the pencil marks. Then screw in your bracket.
8. Line up your shelf on top of this bracket, using your spirit level (horizontally) to make sure it is straight. Mark a line in pencil so you can line up the second bracket.
9. Place your second bracket on the pencil line, then fix it to the wall in the same way as the first one.
10. Place your shelf on top and fix it to the brackets if needed.

Change a light bulb

1. Make sure the light switch is off. Better still, switch off the electricity at the mains for extra safety.
2. Stand on something secure, if the light fixture is on the ceiling or high on a wall.

3. The bulb might still be warm, so use a dry cloth to hold it.
4. If the bulb is a bayonet fitting, push it up gently, then twist it anticlockwise to loosen it. If the bulb is a screw fitting, turn it gently anticlockwise until it comes loose.
5. Have your new light bulb ready. If the bulb is a bayonet fitting, insert it and twist it gently until the bayonet pins slot into place. If the bulb is a screw fitting, insert it and turn it clockwise until it sits firmly in the light socket. Dispose of the old bulb safely.

SHOPPING LISTS

If saving money is essential, or even if you want to simply waste less, consider making a grocery list. Not a scribble on a Post-it note, but something you can update, add to and reshape according to your needs. You can do this by food category (e.g. 'meat', 'pulses', 'dairy', etc.) or by meal planning and buying accordingly.

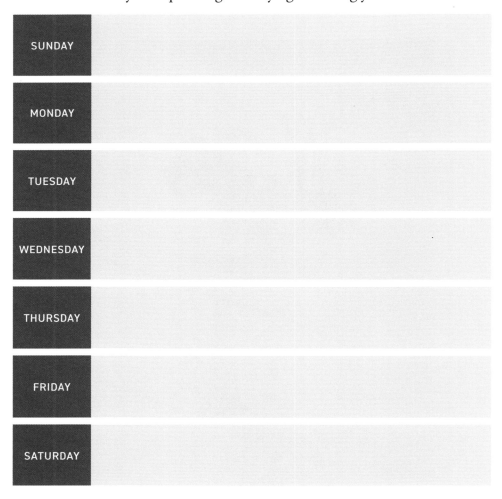

SUNDAY

MONDAY

TUESDAY

WEDNESDAY

THURSDAY

FRIDAY

SATURDAY

It's a good idea to have a list of things you need (or don't need) on hand. I currently have three jars of coffee and two pats of butter because I didn't take my own advice! A few tips:

- Plan your meals for the week so you know exactly what to buy.
- Decide what your spending priorities are, whether it's organic meat or fresh fish, and buy the best quality that you can afford.
- Keep your larder stocked with basics so there's always something on standby.
- Plan your weekly budget in advance. I'm shopping for one, so it's easy for me. If you have a family, your needs will be greater – but you can still save by buying certain high-cost items, like shampoo and washing detergents, when there's an offer on.
- Familiarise yourself with the aisles of your local supermarket to see what's in stock and how much it costs. Look at the *price per kg* to assess this. For instance, a 2kg bag of apples might cost less than a tray of four, depending on brand.
- If budget is a factor, stock up on tinned pulses and staples like rice and pasta. We all need fresh fruit and veg, but it can be easily wasted. I like to use up all my spare veg on a meat-free Monday.
- I'm a divil for getting distracted in the shop by the lovely things on display, but I have to force myself to stick to the list!
- Look for cheaper or 'own brand' versions of items like tinned tomatoes, where quality isn't such an issue – that leaves you more to spend on other things.
- Nominate one or two days in the month for using up everything in the cupboard, before buying more.

Your 'master' meal plan and grocery list might look like this:

PRODUCE	BREAD/BAKERY	DELI	BREAKFAST

BAKING GOODS	CANNED GOODS	CONDIMENTS	SNACKS

REFRIGERATED	MEAT/SEAFOOD	FROZEN	DRINKS

HEALTH/BEAUTY	HOUSEHOLD	MISC.	MISC.

FOOD ON YOUR DOORSTEP

Have you ever tried foraging? You probably have, without even realising it. Picking blackberries, field mushrooms, rosehips, even seaweed – all of this is foraging; that is, picking food that grows in the wild. It might surprise you to know that Ireland is rich in plants and berries that are safe to eat and taste delicious. And you'll be all the more satisfied because you picked them yourself! But before you get carried away and run outside, always, always check that what you pick is edible. Read up on edible plants before you go or, better still, go for a ramble with a professional forager so that you can learn about nature's bounty in more detail. A little bit of research will bring you to any number of experts who can guide you. One very useful website on edible plants is www.eattheweeds.com, which explains how to spot and handle many wild plants.

So, what can you forage to eat?

In the wild

Dandelion leaves I had a friend who was forever picking up big clumps of dandelion leaves in summer. I thought she must have a great passion for them, until she revealed that they were for her pet rabbits! However, dandelion leaves are edible and easy to spot, with that bright yellow flower. A little nibble will reveal that they taste a bit like rocket. If they are too strong in taste for you, mix them in with milder lettuce varieties. But don't forget to wash them! Dogs do like 'using' dandelions …

Curly dock leaves As children we used to use dock leaves to help ease nettle stings. A leaf applied to the spot reduced the itching instantly. They are actually very nice in a salad – they have a slightly lemony flavour. They're a bit like kale in that they need to be 'massaged' (with a squeeze of lemon juice) to soften them. If you mix them with something like wild mint, they'll be delicious. And speaking of wild mint, you'll know it simply by the taste, which is similar to the domestic variety. And you'll be able to smell it, too! The leaves are narrow and pointed and the flowers are purple.

Nettles I used to meet a man on my walks who would wander along the hedgerows, a plastic bag in hand, snipping the tops off all the nettle plants. When I asked him what he was doing, he replied that he was pinching off the tenderest part of the plant to make nettle soup. Without gloves! He was an expert, but I'd always recommend wearing gloves, because nettles do sting. Once exposed to hot water, their sting is neutralised, so they make a great addition to soup, in place of spinach, for example. Make sure that you use tongs to pop them into the stock, so that you don't get stung.

Wood sorrel I can clearly remember eating this as a child and really enjoying that sharp, sour taste. We'd find it on summer walks in the woods and would nibble away on it. It looks very like clover, but the leaves are a bit more rounded and looser. You could try using it like basil in a pesto, to make the most of the flavour – just replace some or all of the basil leaves with sorrel, and blend with olive oil, pine nuts and Parmesan or pecorino cheese. Wild garlic is another easy-to-find plant that really does smell of garlic – you'll see my little piece on it in the month of May in this diary.

Bilberries Another great favourite of ours as children were these blueberry-like berries that grew on little low bushes in the Dublin mountains. Irish people often call them fraughans or fraocháns and they used to grow everywhere, before pine forests took over. I read somewhere that Ireland used to have a very lucrative export business in the fruit, as we had so many. They are harder to find now, but they are still there in little patches. They look very like blueberries, but they are more tart and perfumed in flavour. Try using them in place of blueberries, although you might need to add sugar to taste.

Sloes These dark purple berries are the fruit of the blackthorn tree (*Prunus spinosa*), and you'll know them by their appearance – they look like miniature plums – and by the thorns on the tree! Sloes are picked in October and they can be made into sloe gin. It's easy to make at home: you pop your sloe berries into the freezer (this replicates the frost that makes them release their juices), then you get a nice big bottle, capable of taking 1 litre of gin, 500g of sloes and 250g of sugar. Pop the sloes in first, then the sugar, and finally the gin, screw on the top and give the bottle a gentle swish. Put away under the stairs and once a week or so give it a little shake. If you make it in October, it should be ready for Christmas, when you open it and strain the sloes off, leaving you with a lovely flavoured gin.

Rosehips When I went to Granny's in Co. Sligo, we would always collect rosehips, the bright red fruit of the wild rose. Rich in vitamin C, it would be used to make rosehip tea, rosehip oil and jam, and it was also part of many natural remedies. In fact, in Britain during World War II, people were encouraged to use rosehips to help them get enough vitamin C because other fruit was not available. It's fiddly enough to pick, as I recall, because you have to pull hard to get the rosehips off the tree. Eaten raw, their seeds give them a nasty bitter taste. But they are transformed in a syrup or tea. If you have the time, try making some rosehip syrup. Pick 1kg of rosehips, wash and blitz in a food processor. Add them to 3 litres of water and bring to the boil, then strain the pulp through a muslin cloth or fine-mesh sieve, keeping the juice. Return the pulp to the pan and add 1 litre of boiling water, bring to the boil and then leave it for a few minutes before straining again. You'll now have two bowls of juice. Pour all the juice back into the pan with 500g of sugar and reduce down until you have a fairly thick syrup. When it's cool, pour it into a sterilised bottle or Mason jar. A spoon of this daily will give you more than enough vitamin C.

By the sea

When I looked into wild foraging in greater detail, I discovered that there are all kinds of things by the seaside that are edible and tasty. I'm a conservative eater – and I haven't forgotten the taste of carrageen! – so I needed a little persuading, but once I'd eaten samphire, which grows wild near the beach, I was converted. The other great thing about seaweed, for example, is that it's full of vitamins and minerals, so it's good for you, as well as surprisingly tasty. Make sure that you pick a spot that is pollution-free and not used by doggies. You are safe enough with seaweeds, because they are not generally toxic, but of course *always* check that you know exactly what you are eating when it comes to wild food. If in doubt, check with an expert.

Sea spaghetti Did you know that you can eat sea spaghetti? This edible seaweed is easy to spot, because it looks like dark green spaghetti! You see it swishing around in the water near the shoreline. You can cut it – don't uproot it, so that it can keep growing – then simmer or steam it for ten minutes in boiled water, whereupon it will turn a vivid green, and eat it like actual spaghetti. Or you can chop the cooked seaweed and add it to a stir-fry along with your noodles. The thing with seaweed is that a little goes a long way – try adding a little to your normal diet and you might develop a taste for it.

Sea lettuce This is another tasty seaweed. It looks not unlike frisée lettuce, being bright green and with delicate little fronds. Not to be confused with gutweed, which is also bright green, but has more of a stringy appearance. I haven't tasted sea lettuce, but I'm told that the thing to do with it is to dry it, which you can do in the sun, and crumble it over soups and stews, or eat it as 'crisps'!

Dulse or dillisk This is well known for its health-giving properties. It's often used in seaweed baths and is full of iodine. You'll spot it by its reddish-purple hue and it grows close to the shore on rocks. If you toast it on a dry pan, it tastes like bacon, apparently, and it's not as salty as you might think.

Kelp You'll know this seaweed by its distinctive shape – long, flat ribbons with crinkled edges. You don't need to help yourself to the whole plant; just snip off a section to shred into noodles, or dry it out and blitz it to add flavour to dishes. You can also buy kelp noodles in many supermarkets and speciality shops as a nutritious alternative to wheat-based noodles. The Japanese know it as kombu, and they shred it finely and add it to dashi, or broth.

Sea beet You might spot sea beet on the beach itself. It looks a bit like chard or spinach, with its robust green leaves and reddish stems; you can use it just like spinach, wilted and added to omelettes, or you can chop it and add it to a salad or a stir-fry. Its flowers, which are green or reddish-green, are also edible.

Sea purslane You can recognise sea purslane by its almost cactus-like leaves and long reddish stems; apparently it's very popular with Native Americans, who eat it raw and pickle the stems. You can boil it until tender, which will make it a bit less salty, or you can actually eat it raw, if you're adventurous.

Sea radish With its bright yellow flowers and slender stems, sea radish doesn't look much like a radish, but, like radish, it's a member of the brassica family, which also includes cabbage, turnips and broccoli. It has a very distinctive seed pod, a bit like a pointed broad bean pod, and tastes of both radish and cabbage, which sounds interesting!

COOKING AND STORING FOOD

When my mother was cooking for the five of us and Dad, she had a meal for every day of the week. My brother John used to call Monday's dinner – leftovers from the Sunday roast – 'the lonely dinner'; Tuesday was stew; Wednesday, bacon and cabbage; Thursday was lamb's liver, Friday was fish, of course, and Saturday was a stuffed pork loin. On Sunday, we always ate a roast, but rarely chicken, which was a luxury in those days. We did eat well, as you can see, and there was no processed food. Nowadays, we eat less meat, which is a good thing, I think. So, what if you want to cook from scratch? How can you cook and store safely? www.safefood.eu is home to advice on food safety. Here are some tips:

Cooking meat

- **Whole cuts** like steak don't have to be cooked all the way through, because the bacteria sit on the outside. However, minced meat needs to be cooked all the way through, as does chicken and pork.
- **Cook your steak** on a very high heat to 'sear' it (and kill bacteria) on the outside, so the inside is nice and pink.
- **Cook chicken thoroughly**. Mum's mantra was always 20 minutes per pound weight plus 20 minutes – i.e. 20 minutes per 450g plus 20 minutes. Check that the chicken's cooked by piercing it with a skewer at the thickest point, like the thigh, and check that the juices run clear. If in doubt, slice into it and check that there are no traces of pink.
- **Defrosting chicken** should take 24 hours for a 2.5kg bird – in the fridge. Put any defrosting meat on a large plate to catch any drips that could get onto food below.

- **Hens' eggs** can be eaten raw (if you really must!), say in mayonnaise, or lightly cooked, if you are a healthy adult. Older people, babies and the immuno-compromised should not eat raw eggs. Duck eggs have a higher risk of salmonella, so cook these thoroughly – in 'raw-egg' recipes, like mayonnaise or tiramisu, use hens' eggs.
- **Use separate chopping boards for meat and vegetables**.
- **Wash your hands** thoroughly before and after handling food.

Foods where extra care is needed

Homemade stock Chill quickly and then put it in the fridge. Make sure it's piping hot if reheating.

Shellfish Only buy shellfish from a trusted source; cook it as fresh as you can; discard any with *open shells* before you cook them. When they are cooked, discard any with *unopened* shells. Oysters should be plump and shiny and retreat from your finger when you poke them.

Raw milk and cheese Don't serve to elderly people or youngsters. Pregnant women should avoid them because of the risk of listeria bacteria.

Rice Cook it properly, serve it quickly. If you are reheating it, cool it down quickly, because bacteria can grow at room temperature – I spread it out on a tea tray to cool it, then refrigerate it immediately. When reheating it, make sure it's piping hot. Only reheat rice once.

Chilled foods These need to be handled with more care than frozen foods, because they go off more quickly. Pay attention to the 'use by' dates on these products. Pack/bag them separately from the rest of your shop, so they don't get warm. Store in the fridge – away from fresh foods – and make sure you use them by the 'use by' date. Cook chilled foods until they are piping hot.

Fish Buy fish that is as fresh as can be – nice bright eyes and a shiny skin are good signs of freshness. You don't have to cook it all the way through. According to www.safefood.eu, the bacteria is on the outside of the fish, so the inside can be 'pink' if the outside is well cooked.

RECYCLING – THINGS YOU MIGHT NOT KNOW

- Did you know that soft plastics (such as plastic bags and biscuit wrappers) can't be recycled? They need to go in the bin.
- You can recycle tins, papers, cardboard and rigid plastics.
- Rigid plastics, like bottles and yoghurt cartons, as well as tins, need to be cleaned first as contamination is a big problem in recycling. If you have one dirty container in a batch, it can contaminate the whole lot.
- Make sure that you don't squish everything in. www.mywaste.ie suggests that your recycling should be 'clean, dry and loose'.
- For electronic devices, consult www.weeeireland.ie/household. Here you will find a handy map of centres and retailers where your waste electrical devices can be taken.
- You can donate matching pairs of old shoes (I tie mine together at the laces), clothes and certain soft furnishings (not old sheets or pillowcases) to charity shops. Clothes banks will take more damaged items, which will be shredded and recycled.
- Many councils now offer furniture-removal services for some large items. There is a fee, but it beats a fine for littering!
- There used to be a 'little man' in every street in Ireland who repaired hoovers, washing machines, cookers, even televisions. Those days are gone, but, thankfully, the idea of repairing rather than replacing is taking off again. www.repairmystuff.ie provides a list of places that will repair your devices – everything from lawnmowers to laptops.
- According to MyWaste, Ireland is Europe's top producer of plastic. Oh dear. Let's all try to improve on that. I, for one, have become much more aware of using a 'keep cup' for coffee and a reusable bottle for water, as well as remembering to carry a little tote bag with me to the local shops.

- Your local healthfood store will often have 'refill stations' where you can fill up on household products. Also, refill stores have begun to appear, where you can buy food in bulk. Online stores are great for bulk-buying, say, shampoo, but make sure that the formula works for you before you buy five litres of it.
- I didn't realise how fast 'fast fashion' really is. Some of the larger retailers get daily shipments of new clothes and you can get catwalk looks within a matter of weeks. And most of what we buy is later dumped. So what can we do about it? In Dublin, the Rediscovery Centre, 'the National Centre for the Circular Economy' (www.rediscoverycentre.ie), gives classes in sewing, repairs and even knitting. Sustainable fashion brands help us to shop without a guilty conscience, but many of them are more expensive. Look for pre-loved clothing: it's not just for the charity shops any more – there are some very good online sources of pre-loved wedding dresses, bags, shoes and even designer handbags.

Tips for buying pre-loved clothing

- Do your homework. Look carefully at all the websites and apps to check what they are selling, the quality and price. Get to know the best retailers. Some of the larger ones have quality controls to make sure your item is in good shape.
- Vintage clothing can often be smaller than we're used to, so a size 12 vintage jacket might be a size 8 in today's world. Don't be afraid to ask if the item can be altered.
- Make your dressmaker your best friend. A friend of mine is very small, so she's used to having things taken up and in. You'd be amazed what they can do.
- Check to see a seller's feedback if you're buying online – they must have positive reviews and offer great customer service.

- Look closely at the item to check for any damage, staining or wear.
- Don't buy a ton of clothing from, say, a charity shop just because it's cheap. If you won't wear it, don't buy it.

Eco-friendly alternatives to common household items

Make-up removal pads	Homemade fabric pads or recycled bamboo rewashable pads
Make-up cleansers	Solid make-up removal bars (you can also get shampoo bars)
Cotton buds	Biodegradable, bamboo or thin paper cotton buds
Paper kitchen towels	Old bits of cloth
Batteries	Rechargeable batteries
Plastic rubbish/ dog-poo bags	Biodegradable rubbish/poo bags
Bleach	Baking soda + vinegar
Furniture polish	Beeswax
Disposable razors	Safety razor
Baking parchment	Reusable baking inserts (from kitchen stores and online); available in different sizes
Cling film	Reusable food wraps/jar covers made with beeswax – you can make your own jar covers, which can be washed and reused. My mother used paper jar covers, secured with an elastic band, on jars of jam.

Plastic food boxes	Stainless-steel containers; Mason jars; bamboo lunchboxes
Paper napkins	Fabric napkins
Plastic straws	Stainless steel or bamboo straws
Coffee pods	Compostable coffee pods – but they are expensive. Better still, use ground coffee in a percolator.
Tea bags	Loose tea leaves
Plastic bottles of water	Reusable water bottle made of stainless steel or glass (with a protective sleeve for breakages)

My best recycled and eco-friendly products

DAYS OUT AROUND IRELAND

Over the last couple of years, we've all become much more outdoorsy than we used to be. We now flock to beaches, mountains and other outdoor spots to get fresh air and to enjoy nature. So I decided to include some nice open-air trips and spots for you to visit, to keep up the good work!

Dublin and Leinster

- *St Anne's City Farm and Ecology Centre*, Raheny – a real glimpse of farm life for city kids. They can admire hens, goats, chickens and pigs as well as learn about growing produce. And it's free! www.stannescityfarm.ie
- *Newbridge House and Farm*, Donabate, is another working farm and you can visit the grounds, as well as the house. There's also an adventure playground. www.newbridgehouseandfarm.com
- *Powerscourt Estate*, Co. Wicklow – lots to do here (activities are separately ticketed), with the waterfall, the gardens, the distillery and the Cool Planet Experience, a climate-action exhibition. www.powerscourt.com
- *Newgrange*, Co. Meath. I can still remember visiting Newgrange years ago and being able to walk straight across the fields to the site. Nowadays, it's a lot more organised, but a day trip is well worth the effort, with a shuttle bus to ferry you between the sites, a guided tour and exhibits. Amazing to think that it was built in 3,200 BC – before the Pyramids and Stonehenge! www.worldheritageireland.ie. Don't forget to visit the Hill of Tara on your way home. It's so atmospheric.
- *Lough Boora* is a lovely discovery park in Tullamore, Co. Offaly, full of ponds and wildlife as well as the remains of the former

Bord na Móna peatworks. You can walk on the many trails, hire bikes and there's a café and visitors' centre. www.loughboora.com

- *Athlone Castle*, Co. Westmeath – this impressive castle, smack bang on the River Shannon, was defended by Colonel Richard Grace from the Williamite forces after the Battle of the Boyne. www.athlonecastle.ie
- *Heart-Shaped Lake*, Co. Wicklow – one for the instagrammers! It's a corrie, which is a glacial lake to lay people, and it's off the Old Military Road in Co. Wicklow. It is indeed shaped like a heart and it looks spectacular. However, it does involve a stiff hike up Tonlagee Mountain, and it can be mucky, so not for the faint-hearted or for young children.
- *St Kevin's Way*, Co. Wicklow – not as well known as its neighbour, the Wicklow Way, St Kevin's Way is a 30km route that follows the path of the saint himself from Hollywood, Co. Wicklow, to Glendalough. As you pass through the Wicklow Gap, the scenery is spectacular and when I visited, it was still much quieter than the more popular routes. There's a nice little story about St Kevin's Bed, which is on the route, but which is inaccessible. Apparently, the saint was fast asleep when a maiden came to visit, and he threw her into the lake nearby to show her that he was indeed a saintly man! www.pilgrimpath.ie; www.wicklowmountainsnationalpark.ie/st-kevins-way/
- *Old Rail Trail*, Co. Westmeath. This lovely trail stretches from Mullingar to Athlone, a distance of about 40km, following the old railway beside the canal. The trail is ideal for families, because there are lots of entry and exit points, so you can do smaller sections; Athlone to Moate, for example, is just 8km.
- *Dún na Sí Heritage Park*, near Moate, has lots of natural attractions, from the site of an old hedge school to a wetland park. www.athlone.ie/visit/dun-na-si-amenity-and-heritage-park/

- *Cú Chulainn's Castle*, Co. Louth. Sadly, this isn't his actual castle, but instead the ruins of a house near Dundalk apparently built by a pirate! It's known as Castletown or Dún Dealgan Motte. Rumour has it that the house is built on the remains of the birthplace of Cú Chulainn, hence the name.
- The *South Leinster Way* is a lovely long route for more enthusiastic walkers. It will take you from Kildavin, Co. Carlow to Carrick-on-Suir, Co. Tipperary, a distance of 102km. The countryside is very pretty here, and you'll skirt Mount Leinster on your way. Some of the Way is on the River Barrow, which is lovely, and there are also some really attractive villages to visit, such as Inistioge and Graiguenamanagh, with its open-air pool in the river. www.discoverireland.ie/carlow/the-south-leinster-way

Munster

I'm beginning here with Kerry – and why wouldn't I? I love my adopted home and think that it has so much to offer, but then I'm biased!

- I love visiting the house and gardens in *Kells Bay*. Our microclimate means that we have all kinds of plants that grow nowhere else, and you'll see spectacular examples here of tree ferns and other exotics. It's also home to Ireland's longest rope bridge and it has a nursery and rooms. www.kellsbay.ie
- *Crag Cave* is one that the children will love. Thought to be a million years old, this limestone cave was only discovered in 1983. It has wonderful rock formations and is huge, so you'll spend the whole day exploring. There is also a café, a playground and a bird of prey display. www.cragcave.com
- *Ballaghbeama Gap* isn't as crowded as the Ring of Kerry, being more off the beaten track, but it is just as attractive, with gorgeous mountain scenery, lakes and bogland. Beware, it is

a very windy road, and single-lane, so drive with caution and allow plenty of time for manoeuvres. You will be rewarded with some spectacular views.

- *Skellig Michael* has become such a draw over the last few years that you could be waiting an age to visit, but if you want to see beehive huts without the sheer drop, take a detour to *Fahan*, on the Dingle peninsula, where you can see other examples of these amazing little houses. You can visit Derrynane House, home of Daniel O'Connell, and there's a lovely beach nearby. www.derrynanehouse.ie. If you don't fancy the Cliffs of Moher, I like the cliffs in *Portmagee*, which are spectacular and from which you can see the Skelligs. You can also walk another pilgrim trail, *Cosán na Naomh*, which is 18km from Ventry beach to Brandon Mountain, west of Dingle. It's quite a rugged walk, so make sure you are well prepared.

- In West Cork, the *Béara-Breifne Way* marks the long march of O'Sullivan Beara and his troops after the Battle of Kinsale, in which he was defeated by Queen Elizabeth 1 – and it is *long*, 500km in all, stretching from the Beara peninsula all the way to Blacklion, Co. Cavan. Apparently, of O'Sullivan's 1,000 troops, only 35 finished the march, so you have been warned! You can do little sections of the Way, but you'll need to do your research to find out which are the most developed and which are waymarked trails. You can find a county-by-county guide to all walking trails, complete with information on grades and general advice, at www.sportireland.ie/outdoors/walking/trails; and www.toughsoles.ie has a blog devoted to the walk.

- At the very tip of the Beara Peninsula lies *Dursey Island*, which you can visit by cable car. It's tiny – just a few kilometres in length and about 1.5km wide, but it's a great place for bird-watching, I'm told. You can see guillemots, razorbills, even puffins, which is a real thrill, and it's a great spot to see a whale. Even better is Bull Rock off Dursey Island, home to a large population of gannets. It's well known in the area for the lighthouse, built in the nineteenth century, and for the extraordinary archway cut into the rock face. A boat tour will take you out. www.durseyisland.ie

- *Sherkin Island* is another lovely place, very popular with summer visitors. A highlight is the regatta, usually held at the end of July. Unlike Dursey, Sherkin has a couple of pubs, a church and a primary school for its year-round population of 100. Right in the middle of Roaringwater Bay, the island is a ten-minute ferry ride from Baltimore Harbour, so it's easily accessible. It's known for the arts, as well as its rich marine life. If you keep your eyes peeled, you might see our native lizard there, but the sea is teeming with life: dolphins, basking sharks and even minke whales are often spotted. And if you're really lucky, you might spot the elusive fin whale, which is second only to the giant blue whale in size. www.sherkinisland.ie; www.sherkinisland.eu

- Moving on to Waterford, the *Greenway* will take you on your bicycle from Waterford City to Dungarvan, along the old railway route. The countryside is lovely, and you'll come across Mount Congreve Gardens, a full 70 acres of gardens near Waterford City; you'll pass the Comeragh Mountains and you'll also see Dungarvan Bay and its lovely beach, Clonea Strand, as well as the Durrow Tunnel, which is 382 metres in length – it's no longer in use, by the way, so you can visit safely.

- You can't visit Waterford without learning about its Viking heritage. *King of the Vikings* is a virtual reality experience (www.kingofthevikings.com); there's *Waterford Treasures*, an impressive museum of all things medieval (www.waterfordtreasures.com); there is also great food to be found in this part of the world, and Waterford City was voted Ireland's Foodie Destination 2019, with its own tapas trail, Waterford Harvest Festival and Dungarvan's food festival in springtime.

- The *Ardmore Cliff Walk* is a lovely, easy cliff walk – just 4.5km in length and a nice loop, too. It's part of St Declan's Way, and you'll pass a holy well dedicated to him, after the famous Cliff House Hotel. Keep an eye out for the shipwreck! It's not very old, in case you're thinking of pirates – it ran aground in 1988 and has been there ever since. You'll also see the remains of old watchtowers, one from World War II and one that dates from the Napoleonic Wars, according to local website www.ardmorewaterford.com. Just a little way off the loop lies *St Declan's Monastery*, which is well worth a visit.

- *St Declan's Way* is 96km long, bringing together several old pilgrimage paths, and it will take you from Ardmore to Cashel in Co. Tipperary. It takes in an ancient route, the Rian Bó Phádraig, or the Path of St Patrick's Cow, which the cow apparently dug out with her horns! It's said that St Declan walked the route to meet St Patrick in the fifth century. Waterford is such a pretty county and the rugged Knockmealdown Mountains are very picturesque. Arriving in Cashel, you feel very like the pilgrims of long ago who used to walk this route and many others. www.stdeclansway.ie or www.pilgrimpath.ie

- *Tountinna*, Co. Tipperary is a relatively easy mountain climb in Portroe. Known as the Graves of the Leinstermen Loop, the name is exciting enough! It refers to the King of Leinster and his men, who met a sticky end at the hands of Brian Boru's wife Gormlaith in the year 1000 AD. She ambushed them as they climbed over Tountinna and the King himself is buried there. You'll see Lough Derg in all its glory from the top of this little mountain, as well as the counties of Galway, Tipperary, Clare and Limerick. Worth the climb!

- I was very proud to read recently that Mum's native Co. Sligo had bid for UNESCO World Heritage Status. This is because there are no fewer than 85 Neolithic sites in the county, including the passage tombs at Carrowmore, Knocknashee and Carrowkeel. *The Glen, Culleenamore*, Co. Sligo is a little valley stuffed full of flora and fauna on the side of Knocknarea Mountain. You can climb the mountain easily and visit Queen Maeve's Grave, which was a great favourite of ours as children.

- The '*Lake Isle of Innisfree*' can be viewed from a boat trip along Lough Gill, where my mother lived for many years. I also love to visit *Drumcliff*, where Yeats is buried, when I'm in Co. Sligo. The churchyard is idyllic, with a view of Ben Bulben. My brother Damien has transformed my mother's family farm into a homestead and runs a tour called The Yeats Experience – www.yeatssligoireland.com

- I remember visiting *Mullaghmore*, Co. Sligo, on *At Your Service* with John a few years ago, and it was lovely. It has great water sports facilities and *Bundoran* and *Strandhill* are close by. Mullaghmore has huge waves, so it's also something of a surfing hotspot.

- *Downpatrick Head* in north Co. Mayo is a revelation. The cliffs are terrifying, but the sea stack that stands just offshore is a wonder. It's called Dún Bríste and legend has it that St Patrick hit the cliff with his staff, causing the sea stack to break away. That fellow got everywhere! Mass is celebrated on the site on the last Sunday of July in his honour. You'll also see the Stags of Broadhaven, a collection of huge pointed rocks that stick out of the bay. Beyond the pretty village of Ballycastle, you'll come to the *Céide Fields*, the world's oldest field system at more than 6,000 years old. It's incredible to think that our ancestors were farming in this organised way so many years ago. www.heritageireland.ie/ceide-fields

- The *Erris* peninsula has a lovely looped walk and is a haven for water sports. UISCE, near Belmullet, provides tuition *as Gaeilge* for teenagers in kayaking, windsurfing and so on.

- The *Mayo Greenway* is a track between Westport and Achill Island. It has spectacular views, and winds along for 42km of lovely safe cycling. You can also walk from Newport to Bangor Erris on a walking trail.

- Moving on to Co. Galway, the food scene in *Galway City* is something else, with restaurants like Aniar, Loam, Ard Bia and so on, but Galway is also a great city to wander around, with its little laneways and coffee shops and the nearby strand at Salthill. The International Arts Festival in July is a huge event. www.giaf.ie

- If you like island-hopping, *Inishmaan* is the quietest of the Aran islands – an alternative to Inis Mór and Dún Aonghusa, which can be busy in summer. Inishmaan is home to Teach Synge, the restored cottage of playwright John Millington Synge. Inisheer is tiny, just two square miles, but has lovely beaches and you can hire a bike to see it all.

- *Inishbofin* is another lovely day trip from Cleggan pier in Connemara. Ferries sail regularly from the pier to the island, which is tiny, but packed with history and activities, including a regatta and an arts festival.

- Also in Connemara is the wonderful *Derrigimlagh Bog*, on which Marconi built his first wireless station and which has been transformed into a lovely outdoor museum and looped walk. Alcock and Brown crashed into this bog in 1919 on the first non-stop transatlantic flight – they survived, and there's a monument on top of Errislannan Head close by, with views of the Twelve Bens mountain range.

- If you feel like climbing a mountain, *Diamond Hill* in Connemara National Park is very popular. It has a very well-kept path, but it's steep near the top! Worth it for the views of *Kylemore Abbey* below. The Abbey itself is a great place to spend the day, with a well-tended walled garden, a restored Gothic church and a café. There's also a little bus if the children get tired of walking. www.kylemoreabbey.com

Ulster

- Everyone knows that Donegal has some of the best beaches in the country, such as *Portsalon* beach, but it also has some wonderfully rugged scenery. *Slieve League* is one of the highest cliffs in Europe – three times the size of the Cliffs of Moher! *Fanad Head* lighthouse looks across to the Inishowen Peninsula, home to Malin Head, Ireland's most northerly point. The beach near Fanad, *Ballymastocker Bay*, has been voted the world's second most beautiful beach according to Discover Ireland. *Glenveagh National Park* is huge and full of lovely walking trails. You can also climb *Errigal*, in Gweedore, a mere 750 metres high! It will take you about four hours, and there is some scrambling involved, so come prepared – and watch out for the weather.
- I love the sound of *Turas Cholmcille*, an ancient pilgrim pathway which takes visitors around fourteen standing stones in the valley of St Colmcille, just like the stations of the cross. St Colmcille's Day is 9 June, when local people gather to pay homage to the saint. According to www.pilgrimpath.ie, it's called 'an Turas' and 'is performed barefoot around 15 standing stones and cairns including the saint's own church and bed ... It takes around three hours to complete and the first Turas is usually performed at midnight of Lá an Turais (Day of the

Journey). Some of this pathway is on private land, however, so it's best to check what sections are open and can be visited.

- *Doon Fort* sits right in the middle of Loughadoon, near Ardara. It's a very impressive drystone fort that once housed the O'Boyle clan. A local heritage group has been working to remove ivy from the fort to preserve it, and a boat trip around it will show you how impressive it is.

- Derry is a lovely town steeped in history, and a walk around the old walls of the town will give you a real sense of the place. There's a craft village in the city and the *Museum of Free Derry* tells the story of the city during the Troubles – www.museumoffreederry.org. Not far away is *Mussenden Temple*, on a spectacular cliff overlooking the sea – it was built as a library and is based on a temple in Rome.

- Further east, Belfast is a compact and interesting city, full of things to see, from the well-known *Titanic Experience* and *W5* interactive discovery centre (www.w5online.co.uk) to the Victorian *Linen Hall Library*, which has a range of tours and events and is a lovely building. If you want to get out and about in the city, the *Troubles Tour* is a guided walking tour of the city, led by both Republican and Loyalist former political prisoners, and the famous Black Taxi tours will take you to all of the significant places.

- *Rathlin Island*, 10km off the coast of Co. Antrim, has a mysterious history. Robert the Bruce is meant to have hidden here after being exiled from Scotland in 1306. About 160 people live on the island year-round, but the numbers swell in summer. The *Boathouse Visitor Centre* will tell you all about the history of the island and it's also a paradise for bird watchers. Look out for puffins between April and July. www.rathlincommunity.org is a fount of information on the island.

- Apparently, David Cameron went for a swim in *Lough Erne*, Co. Fermanagh, when the Lough Erne resort hosted the G8 summit in 2013. If that isn't temptation enough, there are many islands to explore in this watery area, including *Devenish Island*, with its sixth-century monastery and round tower. There's a road bridge to Boa Island – not named after the snake, but after Badhbh, goddess of war. You can also get to *White Island* via ferry to admire the carvings on the ruined church.

MY TRAVEL NOTES

60

2022

The Calm after the Storm

Christmas is our busiest time of the year at the Park Hotel Kenmare. We have a full programme for our guests involving afternoon teas, candlelit dinners, visits from Santa, quiz evenings, a mini triathlon and movie night and lots of other entertainment. That all takes quite a lot of organising, so I find myself running around the place, frantically tidying, heading into the kitchen to brief the chef, or talking to John, the barman – who also doubles as a guide to the Kerry Way – about supplies. When all of that madness is over, I breathe a sigh of relief. I love the sleepy days between Christmas and the New Year, and I savour the down time. I like to catch up with my nieces and nephews and find out what they've been up to over the last few months, I like to pick at all the tasty food that I've been missing and to watch a Christmas classic movie (*It's a Wonderful Life* is a particular favourite).

I'm well aware that some of us aren't so lucky to be seeing guests off with a happy wave, delighted to see them go: for many people, it can be a lonely time of year, when they are reminded of less-than-happy events. If you have time on your hands, consider volunteering; you can donate to a local charity, or participate in one of their activities, like walking or swimming, if you can bear it! Here in Kenmare, we have a charity dip from the pier on Christmas morning. If you have an elderly neighbour, knock on their door and see if they need anything, or just wish them a Happy Christmas. At the very least, you'll feel better too!

27 Monday

'No matter how hard the past, you can always begin again.'
Jack Kornfield

28 Tuesday

29 Wednesday

30 Thursday

31 Friday NEW YEAR'S EVE

January

1 Saturday NEW YEAR'S DAY

Happy New Year! I love this quote from Ellen Goodman:
'We spend January 1st walking through our lives, room by
room, drawing up a list of work to be done, cracks to be
patched. Maybe this year ... we ought to walk through the
rooms of our lives, not looking for flaws, but for potential.'

2 Sunday

Nature in Midwinter

I've grown to love winter, because it represents a time of peace and quiet before the busy summer season. I often go for a walk at this time of year and love being outdoors. Here are a few tips to get the most out of those winter outings:

- Set off early. It gets dark at 4pm in wintertime, so I try to get out before lunch. It's better for my mood and ensures I get just a little bit of vitamin D.
- Make sure you're warm enough. A friend of mine is one of those mad all-year-round swimmers, but she would have nothing to do with the Dryrobe craze. Instead, she swears by layers, rather than a single warm covering. So, layer up if you're going out – it costs nothing to take a layer off, but there's nothing worse than being cold. And bring a hot drink. Even better, bring a nice slice of something sweet if you are going on a hike – you'll burn it off with all the walking!
- If you will be out after dark, make the most of any stargazing opportunities. I have a great little app on my phone and if I point it at the sky, it'll tell me exactly what I'm looking at. Also, in Kerry, we have our very own Dark Sky Reserve, where you can see the stars clearly. There's also one in Ballycroy, Co. Mayo, and one in Davagh Forest Park in Northern Ireland.
- I love the winter solstice at Newgrange and have been entering the lottery to see the sunrise there for years. I hope to get lucky one of these days, but in the meantime, the live stream reminds me how spectacular it can be: www.gov.ie/newgrange.

3 Monday

'Winter is a season of recovery and preparation.'
Paul Theroux

---

4 Tuesday

---

5 Wednesday

---

6 Thursday   NOLLAIG NA mBAN

Last year I came across an interview by Marion McGarry of GMIT, on this feast day. Among our many traditions, mothers would wipe the tail of a herring across the eyes of their children to ward off illness! They would also put away all the Christmas decorations, preserving the holly, which would reappear on Shrove Tuesday.

---

7 Friday

---

8 Saturday

---

9 Sunday

If you are trying Veganuary, or even if you are simply trying to reduce your meat intake, here's a hearty soup to keep your energy levels up. Roast 1 sweet potato, 1 red pepper and 1 red onion, diced, seasoned and drizzled with olive oil, for 30 minutes at 190°C/170°C fan/375°F/ gas mark 5. Pop into a blender with 250ml each of stock and coconut milk, add a dash of smoked paprika for warmth, then whizz. Delicious!

This is a lovely poem written by Sigerson Clifford that always reminds me of Mum.

I am Kerry – an extract
I am Kerry like my mother before me
And my mother's mother and her man
Now I sit on an office stool remembering
And the memory of them like a fan
Soothes the embers into flame.
I am Kerry and proud of my name.

My heart is looped around the rutted hills
That shoulder the stars out of the sky
And about the wasp-yellow fields
And the strands where the kelp streamers lie;
Where soft as lovers' Gaelic the rain falls
Sweeping into silver the lacy mountain walls.

My grandfather tended the turf fire
And leaning backward into legend spoke
Of doings old before quills inked history.
I saw dark heroes fighting in the smoke,
Diarmuid dead inside his Iveragh cave
And Deirdre caoining upon Naoise's grave.

(...)

'Twas thus I lived skin to skin with the earth
Elbowed by the hills, drenched by the billows,
Watching the wild geese making black wedges
By Skelligs far west and Annascaul of the willows.
Their voices came on every little wind
Whispering across the half-door of the mind
For always I am Kerry ...

10 Monday

'The good old days were never that good, believe me. The good new days are today and better days are coming tomorrow. Our greatest songs are still unsung.' *Hubert H. Humphrey*

11 Tuesday

12 Wednesday

13 Thursday

This year I promised myself that I wouldn't make any 'must do' resolutions, which I'd forget about by the end of the month. Instead, I would resolve to do only things I want to do: spend more time with friends; work in my garden; listen to more music. That's it!

14 Friday

15 Saturday

16 Sunday

Seville Season

Blink and you'll miss the few weeks when my favourite Seville oranges are in season. I can still remember my mother boiling big pots full of them to make marmalade. If you do make (or have) marmalade, you could use it to make these delicious orange marmalade popovers. The recipe is by my good friend Georgina Campbell, and it's in her book *The Best of Irish Breads and Baking*, but you can find more recipes and information on *Georgina Campbell's Ireland* – www.ireland-guide.com.

Marmalade Popovers

Also known as 'Mum's Muffins'. You need deep bun/muffin tins for this recipe, which is delicious made with homemade marmalade and just right for a tray of 12 – an ideal treat for overnight guests.

Ingredients

3 eggs
175g plain flour
½ tsp salt
325ml milk

l tsp finely grated orange zest
1½ tbsp melted butter or oil
12 tsp marmalade, preferably homemade

Method

1. Make a batter with the eggs, flour, salt and milk – use a processor or blender. Put the eggs in first to prevent the flour sticking to the bowl and mix until smooth.
2. Add the orange zest and melted butter or oil and blend again until thoroughly mixed and smooth, with bubbles rising. Pour into a jug, cover and put aside in a cool place until required.
3. Preheat the oven to 220°C/200°C fan/425°F/gas mark 7. Grease a deep bun/muffin tin well and put the tin into the oven until really hot.
4. Take it out, being careful not to burn yourself. Divide the batter evenly between each muffin casing, filling each one about two-thirds full, then stir a small spoonful of marmalade into each (the marmalade can be warmed slightly if it is too stiff). Put straight into the hot oven.
5. After about ten minutes, reduce the temperature to 180°C/160°C fan/350°F/gas mark 4 and bake for another 20 minutes or until well risen and golden brown.

17 Monday

Did you know that the Saxons called January the Wolf Month? And the first full moon of the year, which shines this evening, is called the Wolf Moon, because wolves would be heard howling at it in the depths of the night.

18 Tuesday

19 Wednesday

I live in an old country house that suffers terribly from mould in the winter and it's a real health hazard. So I cover up with a mask, goggles and gloves (you should see me!) and I attack the affected areas with a 3:1 mix of water and bleach, scrubbing away until a quick wipe will clean it off for good. If you don't like bleach, use one of the many specialist cleaners for the job – checking to see if they stain first!

20 Thursday

21 Friday

22 Saturday

23 Sunday

24 Monday

'Complain that you have no shoes until you meet a man who has no feet.' *Irish proverb*

25 Tuesday

26 Wednesday

27 Thursday

'*Níl sa saol ach gaoth agus toit.*'/'There's nothing in life except wind and smoke.'

28 Friday

29 Saturday

I like to get my garden ready for spring planting at this time of the year. I sweep up any remaining leaves, clean up after the many birds who visit the garden, and tidy up anything I'm going to need in springtime. Then I can reward myself with a cup of tea and a browse of my seed catalogue, ordering lovely things to sow in spring.

30 Sunday

Chinese New Year

I love this festival because it's so exuberant and colourful. The Chinese traditionally marked the passing of time using the lunar calendar, so the New Year came at around the first full moon of the year. Like our own Lá Fhéile Bhríde, the New Year's festival marks the first stirrings of spring, when you'd say a prayer for good weather in the fields. You would also light more than a firecracker or two! A friend who has visited China tells me that the streets of towns and villages are alive with the noise of firecrackers, because people traditionally believed that making noise would scare any lurking monsters or spirits away. Many cities have officially banned them for safety reasons, but that hasn't stopped people! It's as important to the Chinese as Christmas is to the Irish, and because it's a family affair, hundreds of thousands of people will travel home for the holiday – so many that this exodus from cities has its own name: *chunyun*, or 'spring migration'.

This year, 2022, is the Year of the Tiger, a very lucky sign in the zodiac that rules Chinese New Year tradition. Your life will be dictated by whatever sign accompanies your birth year. I was born in the Year of the Snake so, apparently, I'm intelligent and courageous – who knew!

31 Monday

February

1 Tuesday LÁ FHÉILE BHRÍDE/CHINESE NEW YEAR

2 Wednesday

3 Thursday

'Spring is sooner recognised by plants than by men.'
Chinese proverb

4 Friday

By this time of the year, I'm a bit fed up with root vegetables, like parsnip and turnip, so I'm delighted to find purple sprouting broccoli in the shops. Darker and more delicate than its green cousin, it's delicious steamed (put it in the basket when the water has boiled, to avoid overcooking). When it's cooked, run a bit of cold water over it to keep the colour bright. I then add a knob of butter, a squeeze of lemon juice and a good grinding of salt and pepper.

5 Saturday

6 Sunday

*'Life begins the day
you start a garden.'*
Chinese Proverb

Sewing the Seeds

With the worst of the winter now – hopefully – over, I begin my planting indoors in little seed trays. Nothing gives me greater pleasure than to see the first little shoots emerge: a real sign that spring is on its way. Also, planting indoors will protect seedlings from the unpredictable weather and allow them to get a little head start.

I begin by getting together all my little containers for planting my seeds. I use those seed trays that you can buy in the garden centre and even though it might not be eco-friendly, I use plastic because it can be cleaned. I recycle them, if that's any consolation! I also use old yoghurt pots or flower pots – anything that's clean and drains well will do the trick. Then I fill each container up to about half a centimetre from the top with potting compost. I give it a good watering, then leave it to drain, so it's not waterlogged. Now I'm ready to sow. I sprinkle my chosen seeds in, leaving a good 2cm between them if they're big enough, then I pat a little bit of compost over them. Finally, I pop a plastic lid on top – many trays come with ready-made lids; if not, clingfilm or a plastic bag secured with a rubber band will be just fine. I place them on a warm windowsill and I try to remember to move them to a warmer spot at night, when it's chilly. When the shoots appear, whip off the plastic cover, and when you have a few leaves, it's safe to separate them very gently, so that they can grow with bigger gaps between them.

7 Monday

'Ná díol do chearc lá fliuch.'/'Don't sell your hen on a rainy day.' *Irish proverb*

8 Tuesday

9 Wednesday

10 Thursday

Last year I did so much reading and I really enjoyed it. But I can never remember what books I've read! Now I add their titles to my little daily diary and that jogs my memory so I can recommend them to other people. There are also lots of handy apps that will help you to log your favourites and recommend them to others.

11 Friday

12 Saturday

Darwin Day, if you feel like celebrating it, marks the anniversary of the birth of Charles Darwin, father of evolutionary theory, in 1809.

13 Sunday

Doing Our Bit

Trying to be eco-friendly is a challenge I set myself every year. I'll admit that I don't find it easy, but this year I decided it was time to do more. Every little change helps.

- I got the fright of my life watching David Attenborough talk about plastic filling our seas and oceans. So I bought myself a reusable water flask instead of buying plastic bottles; and I cut the tops off old plastic bottles and place some orange slices or sugared water in the bottom for a homemade fly trap, which I place on my kitchen windowsill – it works!
- I have stopped using those plastic cages in my loo – you know, the ones that contain a cleaning agent – instead, I've found one that's like a little bar of soap, with just one plastic arm to go around the rim. I've also found that a mix of bicarb and vinegar makes for a great – and eco-friendly – loo cleaner.
- I've replaced my pod coffee maker with an Italian percolator, which I fill and put on the stove. Yes, it's not as simple, but it tastes just as good – and the grounds are a great addition to my compost heap.
- I have a wormery for my vegetable scraps and eggshells. You can even make your own with a plastic storage crate: drill a few holes in the bottom so the worms can breathe, fill the base with old cardboard and shredded dampened newspaper; pop a layer of compost on top and it's all ready for the worms. If you don't have any, you can order them online, believe it or not!

14 Monday ST VALENTINE'S DAY

St Valentine's Day wasn't always a celebration of love. In Roman times, it was called Lupercalia and it was a celebration of animals and agriculture. Apparently, people sacrificed animals and 'smacked women with animal hides' – personally, I'd prefer a box of chocolates!

15 Tuesday

16 Wednesday

17 Thursday

My healthy eating programme means that I try to eat oily fish three times a week. I love salmon or tuna: tinned tuna with cooked green beans, hard-boiled eggs and baby potatoes makes for a lovely salade niçoise.

18 Friday

19 Saturday

20 Sunday

'In spring, at the end of the day, you should smell like dirt.' *Margaret Atwood*

21 Monday

'You can cut all the flowers, but you cannot keep spring from coming.' *Pablo Neruda*

22 Tuesday

The birthday of Senator Edward (Ted) Kennedy, George Washington, Seán Ó Faoláin and Julie Walters.

23 Wednesday

24 Thursday

After the long winter, my house often feels musty and in need of fresh air. I throw open the windows, but only for 20 minutes or so, or the place turns into a freezer! A nice puff of country air is all that's needed. I also sit down to plan my spring cleaning. I don't try to do everything, but just pick a room that I'm going to freshen up this year and focus on that. Then I can do a really good job on it, rather than trying to do everything and finishing nothing.

25 Friday

26 Saturday

27 Sunday

Antoine Ó Raifteirí

I remember learning this poem in school. It's about a man longing to go home to Mayo, determined to raise the sail as soon as spring arrives. Ó Raifteirí was blind, having got smallpox as a child and he used to wander the roads as an adult, entertaining people with his poems. They were only written down after his death, by Douglas Hyde.

Cill Aodáin – an extract
Anois teacht an earraigh
beidh an lá ag dul chun síneadh,
Is tar éis na féil Bríde
ardóidh mé mo sheol.

Now coming of the Spring
the day will be lengthening,
and after St Bridget's Day
I shall raise my sail.
Antoine Ó Raifteirí

28 Monday

'Study nature, love nature, stay close to nature. It will never fail you.' *Frank Lloyd Wright*

March

1 Tuesday

St David's Day, but also World Compliment Day. So don't forget to say something nice to someone you love – or don't love! When someone pays me a compliment, it cheers me up no end.

2 Wednesday

3 Thursday

Last year, I spotted a little fire extinguisher for sale in my local DIY store, so I bought it and placed it on a wall in the hall outside the kitchen – but then realised I didn't know how to use it, so I took it down and practised (without setting it off!). If you have a fire extinguisher, make sure everyone in your family knows how to use it.

4 Friday

5 Saturday

6 Sunday

Beautiful Boxty

On a trip to Mayo for *At Your Service*, I discovered the pleasures of the humble potato pancake, or farl, or, indeed, boxty. It's popular in Mayo, as well as in Leitrim and further north, and it's delicious. There's a saying that goes: 'Boxty on the griddle, boxty on the pan. If you can't make boxty, you'll never get a man.' It beats Tinder, I suppose! Here's a recipe I found on www.mayo-ireland.ie, so I'm sure it's the best!

Ingredients

750g peeled potatoes
350g self-raising flour
1tsp baking powder
60g butter
Milk or buttermilk to mix
Salt and pepper

Method

1. Grate one half of the raw potatoes into a tea towel and give it a good squeeze. Put the other half on to boil and cook them until soft.
2. Mash the boiled, cooked potatoes, then mix with the grated raw ones. Add the flour and baking powder.
3. Melt the butter, stir into the potato mix and mix to a soft dough, adding enough milk or buttermilk to aid the process. Add salt and pepper to taste.
4. The Mayo recipe calls for the dough to be kneaded as you would soda bread, before being shaped into a round and baked in the oven at 200°C/180°C fan/400°F/gas mark 6 for 20 minutes, but you can also heat a pan with a good knob of butter and pop the boxty on. Keep the pan at a medium heat – don't cook it on high, or else you'll have a crispy outside and a raw inside! Fifteen minutes will give it a nice brown crust and a cooked middle. Cut into four and serve with a nice bit of black pudding and a couple of rashers – or anything you like.

7 Monday

'Real generosity is doing something nice for someone who will never find out.'
Frank A. Clark

8 Tuesday

9 Wednesday

10 Thursday

I don't look forward to this, but now is the time for a good dusting of my fabrics and furnishings. I dust first with a microfibre cloth and only then will I vacuum; if I do it the other way around, I have to vacuum twice!

11 Friday

12 Saturday

During my time at home last year, I became a big fan of 'something on toast' for dinner, now that I didn't have anyone to entertain. I made it cheerful by using the nicest bread I could find and lovely toppings like mushrooms with crème fraîche, homemade baked beans (cannellini beans cooked with a tin of chopped tomatoes, 1 tsp sugar, 1 tsp soy sauce, ½ tsp chilli); smoked fish with cucumber pickles; mashed avocado with hummus and leaves and so on.

13 Sunday

Weird and Wonderful St Patrick's Day Celebrations

I came across a lovely article in the magazine of the Smithsonian Institute in the United States, which revealed all kinds of unusual celebrations of Ireland's national feast day:

- The island of Montserrat in the Caribbean has a large population of Irish descent. They celebrate the day with a Creole breakfast and a Freedom Run, to commemorate the emancipation of African slaves and servants of Irish heritage.
- In Brisbane, Australia, a parade is held in which the locals dress up in the costumes of the Irish tradespeople who built the country: teachers, nurses, carpenters and so on.
- In Japan, the locals in the town of Ise dress up as leprechauns, do jigs and play pipes in a parade that is attended by the Irish Ambassador to Japan.
- My favourite, however, is that of Hot Springs, Arkansas, in which people parade along Bridge Street – 'the shortest street in the world' at 98 feet. Highlights of the parade include Irish Elvis impersonators and Lards of the Dance, a middle-aged dance troupe. What would Michael Flatley think? According to the Smithsonian, 'There's also the "Romancing the Stone" competition, in which the parade-goer with the most original kiss for an impromptu Blarney stone wins a $100 prize. Also making an appearance is Dr Albert Habeeb, who at 95 years old, is the self-proclaimed "World's Oldest Leprechaun".'

14 Monday

On this day in 1773, Oliver Goldsmith's *She Stoops to Conquer* was performed for the first time at the Covent Garden Theatre, London.

15 Tuesday

16 Wednesday

17 Thursday ST PATRICK'S DAY

18 Friday

19 Saturday

20 Sunday

21 Monday

If you're contemplating making a change this year, this is for you: 'The first step towards getting somewhere is to decide you're not going to stay where you are.' *J.P. Morgan*

22 Tuesday

23 Wednesday

I plant my hardy annuals outside about now. I love to have a display of poppies in the summer months. I also plant out the hyacinth bulbs I enjoyed at Christmas. I plant bright chillies in pots because I love the colours. I also love the purple flowers of the chives that I just throw into a pot and that are so easy to grow.

24 Thursday

25 Friday

26 Saturday

The clocks go forward tonight. Daylight saving was introduced in 1916, but did you know that until then, Irish time was 25 minutes behind UK time? It had to do with the passage of the sun, which varied by about that much time between, say, London and Galway. Timetables and the increasing use of clocks meant that that no longer worked, as you can imagine. What is it they say about the Irish approach to timekeeping?

27 Sunday MOTHER'S DAY

George Marion McLellan

I get a daily poem in my email inbox from the Academy of American Poets, which is how I came across this poem by the nineteenth-century African-American poet George Marion McLellan.

A Psyche of Spring

Thou gaily painted butterfly, exquisite thing,
A child of light and blending rainbow hues,
In loveliness a Psyche of the Spring,
Companion for the rose and diamond dews;
'Tis thine, in sportive joy, from hour to hour,
To ride the breeze from flower to flower.

But thou wast once a worm of hueless dye.
Now, seeing thee, gay thing, afloat in bliss,
I take new hope in thoughts of bye and bye,
When I, as thou, have shed my chrysalis.
I dream now of eternal springs of light
In which, as thou, I too may have my flight.

28 Monday

'I've always wanted to go to Switzerland to see what the army does with those wee red knives.'
Billy Connolly

29 Tuesday

30 Wednesday

31 Thursday

April

1 Friday

In France, this day is known as poisson d'Avril – April Fish's Day! Apparently, the whole idea of April fools came about because of the change from the Julian calendar, introduced by Julius Caesar, to the Gregorian one, which was Pope Gregory XIII's invention. The reason for this is because the Julian Calendar was out of sync with the seasons, with the New Year beginning at the same time as the spring equinox and Easter being at the wrong time for Pope Gregory. So the new calendar began on 1 January and the April Fools, according to history, were those who were slow to get the message.

2 Saturday

3 Sunday

Francis Ledwidge

Francis Ledwidge is known as the 'poet of the blackbirds' because of his love of the landscapes and nature of his home in Co. Meath. He joined the British Army during World War I and died in Belgium on 31 July 1917.

A Rainy Day in April

When the clouds shake their hyssops, and the rain
Like holy water falls upon the plain,
'Tis sweet to gaze upon the springing grain
And see your harvest born.

And sweet the little breeze of melody
The blackbird puffs upon the budding tree,
While the wild poppy lights upon the lea
And blazes 'mid the corn.

The skylark soars the freshening shower to hail,
And the meek daisy holds aloft her pail.
And Spring all radiant by the wayside pale
Sets up her rock and reel.

See how she weaves her mantle fold on fold,
Hemming the woods and carpeting the wold.
Her warp is of the green, her woof the gold,
The spinning world her wheel.

4 Monday

'I am currently under construction. Thank you for your patience.'
Anonymous

5 Tuesday

6 Wednesday

7 Thursday

8 Friday

I used to love preparing an Easter egg hunt in the garden for my nieces and nephews. I would find all kinds of ingenious places for all the chocolate I bought, and one year I couldn't find one of the larger eggs because it was so well hidden. It's in the garden to this day, but I can't imagine it's still edible!

9 Saturday

10 Sunday

*'Nothing inspires
cleanliness more than
an unexpected guest.'*
Radhika Mundra

Baking Easter Delights

When I was a child, Dad was always busy working in the shop he owned in Stepaside, but the one advantage was that we got our Easter eggs early. We only got one each, but that was a huge treat. He would wrap them all in brown paper and Mum would put them on the highest bookshelf in the sitting room. We'd watch them for weeks beforehand in anticipation of the big day. To this day, I love making Easter treats with children, because they are fun and because they involve chocolate.

I like making really simple Easter egg nests as they look lovely and can be decorated to your heart's content. All you need is Shredded Wheat (the large ones, not the mini sort), 400g of chocolate and mini Easter eggs or other edible decorations of your choosing. Break up the Shredded Wheat into a bowl, then melt the chocolate in a heatproof bowl over a pan of simmering – not boiling – water. Pour it over the cereal, stir to mix, then place a rounded dessertspoon into a paper case. Make a hollow with the back of a spoon and, when the nests are set, fill with eggs, jellies or even edible flowers. I love buying edible cake decorations and have to stop myself filling the cupboards with them.

And if you're weighed down with leftover chocolate after Easter, melt 250g in a saucepan over a gentle heat, along with 100g butter and a couple of tablespoons of golden syrup. Add 100g of bashed-up digestive biscuits, stir, then pour into a container lined with clingfilm. Pop into the fridge for a couple of hours, then decorate with mini eggs.

11 Monday

'Life isn't about waiting for the storm to pass. It's about learning to dance in the rain.'
Vivian Greene

12 Tuesday

13 Wednesday

14 Thursday HOLY THURSDAY

15 Friday GOOD FRIDAY Hopefully, the soggy fish of our childhoods is a distant memory; I still eat fish on Good Friday, but I make sure to buy a nice fillet of cod (sustainably sourced), which I slice into thick fingers, coat in seasoned flour, dip into a beaten egg, then into a dish of white breadcrumbs, which I've quickly zapped in the food processor. To be extra healthy, I pop them on to a rack over a baking sheet and cook at 200°C/180°C fan/400°F/gas mark 6 for 15 minutes. Delicious served with mayonnaise.

16 Saturday EASTER SATURDAY

17 Sunday EASTER SUNDAY

Easter Traditions in Ireland

Easter is a big holiday, no matter what your beliefs: a celebration of food, family and friends. In Ireland, we love roast lamb, chocolate, hot cross buns ... but many of our old traditions evolved before and during Christianity and lived alongside it.

Before the advent of branded chocolate Easter eggs, children had their own Easter celebrations. They would go from house to house collecting what would have been big treats in those days, like eggs, or slices of cake, even bread and butter, whatever their neighbours had available, and they'd find a little spot in the fields to have a big feast. I came across a lovely memory in the Folklore Collection in UCD, from a lady called Kathleen Murray, in Delvin, Co. Westmeath. In immaculate writing, she recalled the blessing of salt and water on Easter Sunday. The salt was then sprinkled on animal feed, in the hope of keeping disease at bay; the water was sprinkled on the crops in the hope of a good harvest. She also referred to the sun 'dancing' on Easter morning, when people would walk to the nearest holy well to observe its reflection in the water, doing a jig! In the afternoon, people would attend a cake dance, which was exactly that: a hooley to music in which the best dancers would win a beautifully decorated cake made for the competition.

18 Monday EASTER MONDAY

'Friends come and go, like the waves of the ocean, but the true ones stay, like an octopus on your face.' *Anonymous*

19 Tuesday

20 Wednesday

I love to use up any Easter lamb in a homemade kebab. I buy flatbreads in the local shop, shred some cold lamb into the middle of one, add some pickled red onion, a tablespoon of hummus, a dash of paprika and a handful of shredded lettuce. Hey presto – a quick and handy lunch.

21 Thursday

22 Friday

23 Saturday

24 Sunday

25 Monday

'If you have only one smile in you, give it to the people you love.' *Maya Angelou*

26 Tuesday

27 Wednesday

April is a wonderful time in nature. Every little bird and animal seems to be busy. It's the start of the basking shark season; migrating birds like house martins, swallows and swifts are returning and you might even hear the distinctive call of the cuckoo. Also, according to www.irelandswildlife.com, you might be lucky and spot a red squirrel or even 'the elusive Irish stoat'. It also amused me to see that Dublin Airport's long-stay car park is a 'hotbed of hare activity'!

28 Thursday

29 Friday

30 Saturday

The birthday of filmmaker Jane Campion, country singer Willie Nelson and novelist John Boyne.

May

1 Sunday

May Day

May Day is International Labour Day and it celebrates the humble worker, but many cultures celebrate much older traditions and many of these have actually been revived in modern times. In Ireland, Bealtaine celebrated the transition from the gloom of winter to the sun of late spring with bonfires. One tradition was to drive cattle between two bonfires, guaranteeing good health for the rest of the year. In Edinburgh, they celebrate Bealtaine with the Festival of Fire, but it's also traditional to climb the steep hill of Arthur's Seat at the edge of the town on May Day. Apparently, if you wash your face in the morning dew, you'll be beautiful for ever. I must try it!

May Day's pagan roots run deep, with a belief that the October festival of Samhain marked the beginning of the 'death' of winter and Bealtaine the life of summer. In England, dancing around the maypole is still a popular tradition, but did you know that we also danced around the maypole in Ireland? It's thought that the tradition came to Ireland via English and Scottish settlers. A couple of centuries ago, there was a maypole in Harold's Cross, in Dublin, as well as near the Botanic Gardens in Glasnevin. Today, Holywood in Co. Down is home to the only surviving maypole on the island of Ireland and young people decorate it with ribbons and dance around it to this day.

2 Monday MAY BANK HOLIDAY

'I am an optimist. It does not seem to be much use to be anything else.'
Winston Churchill

3 Tuesday

4 Wednesday

5 Thursday

I have a confession to make: when my granny died, I inherited her precious china cabinet, but it would be years before I gave its contents a good clean. She was so proud of her little collection, and so was I, once I'd done the work of polishing her best silver teapots and washing her china in warm soapy water. I finally felt that I'd done her proud.

6 Friday

7 Saturday

8 Sunday

Alfred, Lord Tennyson

Alfred, Lord Tennyson, was one of the most famous individuals of the Victorian age and a great favourite of Queen Victoria. This long poem 'went viral' as we'd say today, quickly becoming a classic, and it was often set to music.

The May Queen – an extract
The honeysuckle round the porch has woven its
    wavy bowers,
And by the meadow-trenches blow the faint sweet
    cuckoo-flowers;
And the wild marsh-marigold shines like fire in
    swamps and hollows gray;
And I'm to be Queen o' the May, mother, I'm to be
    Queen o' the May.

The night-winds come and go, mother, upon the
    meadow-grass,
And the happy stars above them seem to brighten as
    they pass;
There will not be a drop of rain the whole of the
    livelong day;
And I'm to be Queen o' the May, mother, I'm to be
    Queen o' the May.

All the valley, mother, 'll be fresh and green and still,
And the cowslip and the crowfoot are over all the hill,
And the rivulet in the flowery dale 'll merrily glance
    and play,
For I'm to be Queen o' the May, mother, I'm to be
    Queen o' the May.

9 Monday

'Be like a flower and turn your face to the sun.' *Kahlil Gibran*

10 Tuesday

11 Wednesday

12 Thursday

I became very aware of the importance of kindness during the last couple of years. Whether you're a fan of random acts of kindness or simply your good deed for the day, try to do just one nice thing for someone else today: take in their online parcel if they are at work, tidy their grass verge as well as your own, or help an elderly neighbour with their wheelie bin.

13 Friday

14 Saturday

15 Sunday

16 Monday

'When everything seems to be going against you, remember that the airplane takes off against the wind, not with it.' *Henry Ford*

17 Tuesday

18 Wednesday

19 Thursday

I like lighter dishes at this time of the year. If you haven't tried ceviche, a Peruvian seafood dish, or you're put off by raw fish – don't be. As long as it's completely fresh, the delicious 'cooking' of the fish in lemon juice is heaven. All you need to do is to squeeze the juice of a lemon or lime over thin strips of the raw fish, making sure it's fully covered (one lemon per 75g of fish is about right), then pop it in the fridge for half an hour. Serve with a lovely summer salad. Delicious!

20 Friday

21 Saturday

22 Sunday

I usually organise my hot press at this time of year, taking all the linen out and checking it for any stray stains or musty smells. Then I weed out all of the stray pillowcases that no longer have a matching duvet cover, the worn sheets and frayed towels and I recycle them – if they're respectable – or turn them into dusters. Then I try to put all of my duvet sets together and pop them in a labelled basket, before placing it back on the shelves.

The Hungry Gap

When I was a child, the time between March and early June was normally a time of boring food, because the root veg of winter would be gone, but the lovely summer produce had yet to arrive. During this hungry gap we made the most of whatever was to hand. Even nowadays, when you can get food from all over the world, it makes sense to eat local. In May, I love nothing better than a bowl of new potatoes, with their flaky skins coated in a good knob of butter, and I've become a bit of a fan of wild garlic, which grows abundantly in Ireland. I love the glossy green leaves and tiny white flowers. It's quite pleasant, like a milder version of a garlic clove. Donegal chef Zack Gallagher has a very useful section on wild garlic on the Irish Food Guide website (www.irishfoodguide.ie), with lots of pictures. If you want to give cooking with this plant a go, you can shred it and add to soups, or as a novel replacement for basil in pesto.

And thank God for asparagus! I look forward to eating the big, fat spears that are so delicious. Don't forget to trim the woody bits at the bottom – if you bend the spear gently, it will snap off and leave you with the tender top half. You can then steam the spears or, better still, cook them standing on end in a saucepan filled with two inches of salted water. By the time the bottoms are cooked – 3–5 minutes depending on how fat they are – the tender tops will have steamed beautifully. Don't over-cook them, or you'll end up with mush.

23 Monday

'I always wanted to be somebody, but now I realise that I should have been more specific.'
Lily Tomlin

24 Tuesday

25 Wednesday

The birthday of Cillian Murphy, Ralph Waldo Emerson and US Senator Amy Klobuchar.

26 Thursday

27 Friday

I try to make the most of the long evenings at this time of year. They are gone soon enough! I like nothing better than a brisk walk after dinner, armed with a pair of binoculars to help me spot any wildlife.

28 Saturday

29 Sunday

Growing Tomatoes

It's something of an annual project of mine to grow my own crop of tomatoes, but I am generally foiled, because of the amount of travel I do – in a normal year, that is. Either the poor things are left dry and wilting, or the damp, dull weather sees them off. But every year I try again! I begin with a selection of tomato plants, which I buy at my local garden centre. This might seem like cheating, but I like to think of it as getting a head start. Make sure the plants are healthy, about nine inches in height, and in a nice roomy pot to give them plenty of space. I water them carefully: not too much, so the roots get soggy; and not too little, so the poor things dry out. To test, I lift the pot up and if it's very light, time for a water! The soil should be moist, not soaking wet. As the plants grow, you will need to increase the watering – tomatoes are thirsty. And keep them warm – if the weather is still chilly, cover your plants at night. Finally, use a nice, rich food to keep them healthy – I use liquid from my wormery. And make sure that they get plenty of sun when the weather warms up – tomatoes love sunshine.

If you want to encourage children to grow plants, it's best to start simple. In fact, I once came across a lovely article, entitled 'What Plants Survive Kids', which made me laugh. Sunflowers are a great idea, as they are hardy enough and will be spectacular when fully grown; nasturtiums are another easy-to-grow plant with lovely flowers; and radishes are a cinch.

30 Monday

'Inside of me, there's a thin person struggling to get out. But I can normally sedate him with four or five cupcakes.' *Bob Thaves*

31 Tuesday

June

1 Wednesday

For a quick midweek supper, I make a small omelette with two eggs, a splash of milk and a twist of salt and pepper, then I use it instead of a wrap, packing it full of smoked salmon and rocket, or dabs of goat's cheese and sundried tomato – tasty and nutritious!

2 Thursday

3 Friday

4 Saturday

When I was a child, we would often go strawberry picking. There was a fruit farm in Rathfarnham, as I recall, and we'd cycle up there, returning with bags and baskets full of the sweet fruit. They are delicious with cream, of course, but I love them with a drizzle of balsamic vinegar, which brings out their sweet flavour, or with a creamy cheese like ricotta, drizzled with honey.

5 Sunday

'To plant a garden is to
believe in tomorrow.'
Audrey Hepburn

Al Fresco Dining

I found that being able to sit outside in the evenings was an absolute godsend during my little 'unscheduled' holiday last year. Watching the swallows swoop overhead and enjoying the warm breeze really cheered me up. I also developed a few handy routines for outdoor eating so that I could make the most of the good weather.

I became a dab hand at making one-pan suppers, like a chicken traybake, or salmon in tinfoil or parchment parcels, which I'd drizzle with olive oil and place on a bed of veg and pop into the oven for 20 minutes or so. Robust salads like tricolore (mozzarella, basil and sliced tomato) and cold pasta pesto salad were also great. Dessert was as simple as I could make it: seasonal fruit, or a slice of lemon tart that I'd picked up in the bakery.

If I was having friends over – when the rules allowed – I kept things simple, using no-fuss melamine plates and a bowl of summer flowers on the table. I had a very handy set of plastic wineglasses that I got from a picnic set – although I am not ashamed to serve wine in a tumbler if needs be – they will stay upright outdoors! And of course, it being Ireland, heat is a big deal. I bought a patio heater last summer, after hunting for one for months, and it's been a blessing – but do your research as they can eat electricity. I found an infra-red one to be the best value. A friend of mine spent a month building her very own pizza oven in the garden, which now doubles as a lovely source of warmth. A brilliant idea!

6 Monday JUNE BANK HOLIDAY

'The summer night is like a perfection of thought.'
Wallace Stevens

7 Tuesday

8 Wednesday

9 Thursday

10 Friday

Who wants to spend summer inside, cleaning? Not me!
However, I do keep on top of the essentials. I sprinkle
the bottom of my bin with baking soda to catch any
whiffs, I try to keep the windows clean and streak-free,
and I dust regularly to keep allergies at bay. Simple.

11 Saturday

12 Sunday

Bugs and Other Nuisances

At this time of year, my garden is full of insects, some of which make their way indoors. They can be a real nuisance. This always reminds me of one of my favourite ever trips, to a plantation house deep in the jungles of the Yucatan peninsula in Mexico. At the time, I was a member of the Small Luxury Hotels of the World group, and I was deputised to go to a former sisal plantation on the Yucatan peninsula to assess a new member.

We flew to Merida and, after a long drive, we arrived at a clearing, in which was the most magnificent colonial house. It was spectacular – brightly coloured, with lots of period features, including a group of little cottages that had belonged to workers on the plantation. When sisal was the fibre of the moment in the nineteenth century, it was used in everything from ropes to bags. The death of that industry, when it was replaced by plastic, had meant the death of this way of life, but our hosts were restoring this little bit of colonial heritage to its former glory. What fascinated me was the air-conditioning system between living room and bedroom, which consisted of a cold plunge pool. You'd immerse yourself in it to cool down before going to bed! But the best innovation of all was the little trough that surrounded the estate. About two feet across and eighteen inches deep, it was filled once a week with water, which would attract mosquitoes, which would lay their eggs on it. The following day, it was emptied, along with the mosquitoes and their eggs. What a genius idea!

13 Monday

'The present moment is filled with joy and happiness. If you are attentive, you will see it.' *Thích Nhất Hạnh*

14 Tuesday

15 Wednesday

I love a salad on a sunny day. I've never liked watermelon as a fruit, but in a salad it's a revelation. Try it with cubes of feta or grilled halloumi and torn mint leaves. If I have any stale white bread, I use it to make the delicious Italian salad panzanella – chunks of torn-up ciabatta or baguette, mixed with olive oil, basil and fresh tomatoes from the garden.

16 Thursday

17 Friday

18 Saturday

19 Sunday FATHER'S DAY

20 Monday

'Spring being a tough act to follow, God created June.'
Al Bernstein

21 Tuesday

22 Wednesday

23 Thursday

24 Friday

If my fridge is smelling a bit, I stick a small open jar of baking soda on one of the shelves. It's brilliant at absorbing odours. Half a lemon upside down on a saucer is also handy, as is regular cleaning. I like to use vinegar to wipe the shelves down.

25 Saturday

26 Sunday

Salad Days ~ Growing Your Own Green Leaves

I used to be an awful man for buying bagged salad leaves until I learned how to grow my own, and I try to do this every summer. It's really very easy, and there's nothing nicer than having your own supply to add colour and crunch to your plate. You don't need to have a big vegetable patch; you can grow salad leaves in containers. Don't forget drainage, which is important with containers. Pop a layer of stones at the bottom of any larger pots to aid drainage. Compost is your friend when growing in containers – ask your garden centre for advice here – and if you have homemade compost, all the better. I nourish my leaves with my wormery liquid and it really encourages them to grow.

Cut-and-come-again varieties of lettuce are brilliant – you snip off however many leaves you need, and they regrow. If you are planting seeds, remember that they need light to germinate, so you'll just need to scatter them on top of the soil, brushing over a light layer to keep them from blowing away. I have also had success by mixing two types of plant – sweet peas with runner beans, for example, or peppers with parsley. Some plants don't like being together, however, like taller and smaller ones, or plants that need watering close to plants that don't.

27 Monday

'I want my children to have all the things I couldn't afford. Then I want to move in with them.' *Phyllis Diller*

28 Tuesday

29 Wednesday

30 Thursday

I find fruit flies an awful pest at this time of year, so I've adapted a little trick from Martha Stewart. I put a couple of tablespoons of apple cider vinegar at the bottom of a jar, cover it in clingfilm and prick a few holes in the top. The little beasts will fly in and not fly out again!

July

1 Friday

2 Saturday

3 Sunday

A Fourth of July Barbecue

I spend a part of every year in the States, drumming up business for Tourism Ireland, and it's something I love doing. I still find America a country of great optimism and energy. I love celebrating the Fourth of July, too, because who doesn't love fireworks, a lovely summer's evening and a barbecue?

- Burgers you make yourself with mince bought loose from the butchers, with lots of fat for flavour, are much tastier than pre-made ones. I like to keep the fat from frying a rasher to bind the beef, along with a few white breadcrumbs and an egg.
- Fish is brilliant on a barbecue, too; one of my favourite ideas comes from a friend of mine, who always barbecues her fish in newspaper, because it really helps to keep the moisture in. She cooks the fish whole, stuffed with lemon and lime slices, herbs, a good grinding of salt and pepper and a slug of olive oil, wrapped nice and tight, then placed under a running tap until the package is damp, before popping onto the barbie. Twenty-five minutes later, you'll have lovely, moist fish. Delicious.
- Cauliflower steaks are a brilliant veggie main; they keep their shape really well on the barbecue and taste delicious with that smoky flavour. Thickly sliced sweet potatoes are also great, as are portobello mushrooms and red peppers. Anything that's robust. I saw a great tip somewhere about skewering the veg together on the grill, so that you can just flip them over, instead of turning them individually.

4 Monday INDEPENDENCE DAY, USA

This day celebrates American independence from Britain in 1776. Thomas Jefferson drafted the Declaration of Independence and Americans celebrated by hosting mock funerals of the British king, George III, with bonfires, parties and parades.

5 Tuesday

6 Wednesday

7 Thursday

I love summer fruit. My favourite time of the year is cherry time. They can be very expensive, so I just buy a few and really enjoy them. I eat them fresh by themselves, or with a mild cheese, like goat's cheese. A tin of black cherries warmed gently with a dash of brandy for a few minutes makes a delicious dessert with ice cream. I know it as Cherries Jubilee, so it must have something to do with the queen!

8 Friday

9 Saturday

10 Sunday

Happy Camping

I can still remember my first ever 'foreign' holiday, when I went camping on the Isle of Man with a schoolfriend. I must have been 16 or so and I can still remember that Mum was terrified at the prospect of me going off to the wilds with a tent!

We were quite well prepared, as I recall, lugging one of those heavy canvas tents that were all the rage in the 1960s as we headed off on the ferry. We'd booked a campsite in Laxey, which was a very picturesque spot, complete with a waterwheel and old railway – not that we saw either, because from the moment we arrived to the moment we left, it bucketed down with rain. The tent was a nightmare to put up, because it was so heavy, but we'd bought it because it had a built-in groundsheet, which was just as well because of the sodden ground. We had to do all our cooking inside, because of the howling gale and horizontal rain, and my friend Brian became a dab hand at cooking fish fingers on our primus stove, the only thing we could find in the local shop. I was not a happy camper!

Mum had friends on the Isle of Man, who took pity on us and invited us to Sunday lunch, which was a full roast dinner, complete with Yorkshire pudding and all the trimmings. We felt a lot better drying out in their living room, until the lady of the house handed me a glass of what I thought was Coke. It turned out to be a drink called dandelion and burdock, which tastes of Vick's. I couldn't help it, I spat it out onto the table. I arrived back in Dublin wet, grimy and vowing never to camp again.

11 Monday

'Ní neart go cur le chéile.'/'There is no strength without unity.' Irish proverb

12 Tuesday

13 Wednesday

14 Thursday

15 Friday

If you go camping, make sure to bring a nice roomy tent – if there are four of you, buy a six-person tent so you have room for all your gear. Pick a style that will be easy to erect in a force seven gale, but sturdy enough to withstand it, and bring chairs! A friend of mine brought the entire contents of her kitchen but forgot anything to sit on – little camping chairs are great. Other essentials are a torch, matches and a multitool that can serve as a knife and fork, bottle opener, etc.

16 Saturday

17 Sunday

18 Monday

19 Tuesday

20 Wednesday

I love a glass of fizz in July – lemonade, that is! I use lemons, fizzy water and honey, not sugar – it tastes delicious and is really refreshing. I use four lemons, juiced, for each litre of water, and I add the least amount of honey I can manage. If added sugar is an issue for you, Jamie Oliver recommends stevia, a natural plant sweetener. You can buy it in the supermarket nowadays.

21 Thursday

22 Friday

23 Saturday

24 Sunday

School's Out for Summer (and the House is a Mess!)

Keeping the house clean and tidy should be easier in summer. After all, we spend more time outdoors and less time on the sofa. However, friends of mine with children tell me that summertime can be tricky, with kids at home from school for months, trailing their stuff in and out all the time. The plates, cups and bowls gather under beds and the crumbs and spills decorate the counter ...

One pal suggests giving each child a summer task to do. No matter how small, everyone can do something. Little hands can fold socks, bigger hands can use a duster, or run the hoover around, or feed the dog. Use everyone to make life easier, even in tiny ways. It will also set them up for independence.

A friend of mine with teenagers used to leave a note on the kitchen counter before vamoosing to work. Each child was asked to do one thing by the time she got home. Just one thing – she wasn't being too ambitious. Of course, it was all done five minutes before her return, but it was done!

One of my mother's rules was 'one in, one out', which meant that if we wanted to take something out to the garden, we had first to put something away; if we wanted to take our bikes out for a spin, we had to put the tennis rackets away in the cupboard under the stairs. She was a stickler for this, or else the garden would have been full of bicycles and tennis rackets.

25 Monday

26 Tuesday

27 Wednesday

If you'd like to find jobs for your children to do, try getting them to sort the laundry into whites and colours; watering the plants is another easy task, and hard to overdo in summer; making their own beds every morning is another job they can get into the habit of doing.

28 Thursday

29 Friday

Can you believe that the days are already getting shorter? Now is the time of the year to savour every last drop of daylight.

30 Saturday

31 Sunday

Day Trippers

Summer is high season at the Park Hotel Kenmare and we don't have a spare minute, but if I do get a break, I like to plan a short trip somewhere. Some of my fondest summer memories are of day trips to the beach with Mum and Dad or to our friends in Malahide, when the sun shone and the day just seemed to stretch ahead – impromptu events often give us the happiest memories, I find. And I always pack a picnic: there's truly nothing nicer than eating your own sandy sandwiches on the beach, or tucking into a slice of quiche in the shelter of your car!

I start by making a list of things to bring, before I even think about food. I have a thick picnic blanket, which has a reflective undersurface and folds away into a neat little bag. I have a lovely picnic rucksack that my nephew gave me, which came with sturdy plastic plates, glasses, knives, forks, spoons, and even a little cheeseboard and knife in its own pocket! It also has a very handy cooler bag attached to the side for my chilled drink – excellent. Cooler bags, or those handy iced blocks that you can take out of the freezer, are great for keeping things cool – a friend of mine freezes water in small water bottles for the same purpose and they double as drinks. Oh, and don't forget a bottle opener!

When it comes to food, I keep things simple. I just buy a nice crusty baguette, a good strong Irish Cheddar, fruit that won't squash, like apples, grapes or pears (no bananas!) and a chunk of fruit cake. I like to have a cup of tea, so I have one of those handy thermoses that keep liquids hot or cool as desired.

1 Monday AUGUST BANK HOLIDAY

2 Tuesday

'Never have more children than you have car windows.'
Erma Bombeck

3 Wednesday

4 Thursday

In August, my garden begins to take on a bedraggled air, with blooms past their best and the leaves dusty. I spend a couple of hours outside tidying, giving my veg a good feed in the hope that it will produce a little more, watering if it's been dry and organising my stock of bulbs for the spring. The garden is never static; it changes every day.

5 Friday

6 Saturday

7 Sunday

The Last Rose of Summer

Thomas Moore's 'The Last Rose of Summer' is one of my favourite poems, and one I remember singing in school. It always feels very poignant as summer draws to a close.

'Tis the last rose of summer,
Left blooming alone;
All her lovely companions
Are faded and gone;
No flower of her kindred,
No rose-bud is nigh,
To reflect back her blushes
Or give sigh for sigh!

I'll not leave thee, thou lone one.
To pine on the stem;
Since the lovely are sleeping,
Go, sleep thou with them;
Thus kindly I scatter
Thy leaves o'er the bed,
Where thy mates of the garden
Lie scentless and dead.

So soon may I follow,
When friendships decay,
And from love's shining circle
The gems drop away!
When true hearts lie wither'd,
And fond ones are flown,
Oh! who would inhabit
This bleak world alone?

8 Monday

'Procrastinate now. Don't put it off.' *Ellen DeGeneres*

9 Tuesday

10 Wednesday

I love the perfumed smell and taste of elderberries, which are in season about now. They can't be eaten raw, but they are delicious cooked. My friend's mum used to make wine with hers, but I prefer a syrup: you'll need 500g each of berries and caster sugar, and the juice of a lemon. Cook the fruit for 20 minutes, by itself, just covered with water, then cool and strain, adding the sugar, then tipping both into the pot for another ten minutes to reduce down. It's like a cordial, delicious with fizzy water.

11 Thursday

12 Friday

13 Saturday

After a busy summer at the hotel, I like to tidy my pantry and reorganise my fridge. I clear out any old jars that have been hanging around, remove any mouldy veg or gone-off food, and give the fridge a good clean using just a drop of washing-up liquid in hot water with a splash of vinegar.

14 Sunday

15 Monday

'The only way to have a friend is to be one.' *Ralph Waldo Emerson*

16 Tuesday

17 Wednesday

Around now, I'm beginning to think about my crop of winter veg. If I plant now, I will – hopefully – be assured a supply of veg just when I most need it. I love chard, because of its bright yellow and red stems, and it's easy to grow. I also love growing spinach and it's a great winter survivor. Be sure to use netting to protect the plants from pigeons and use beer traps for slugs. At least they'll have a happy death!

18 Thursday

19 Friday

20 Saturday

21 Sunday

A Little Bit of Sweetness

At the end of August, my mum would busy herself picking our annual crop of gooseberries. I hated them! To me, they tasted horribly bitter and dry. But a gooseberry fool was another matter. The addition of caster sugar and cream transformed this maligned fruit into something delicious. She would get roughly half a kilo of the fruit, wash it, pop it into a saucepan with just a couple of tablespoons of water and about four tablespoons of sugar (taste to check for sweetness). The mixture would bubble away on the stove for ten minutes, before being set aside to cool down. Mum would then whip a carton of cream until it was firm but still soft and fold the fruit into it. (She used single cream, but 250ml of double cream is even better!). And that was it. Unbelievably simple. I also discovered the pleasures of roasting stone fruit a couple of years ago – it's a great way of using tart or underripe fruit. All you need to do is pop the stoned, halved fruit of your choice onto a roasting tray and drizzle it with a dessertspoon or two of honey and a teaspoon of vanilla essence. Pop into a hot oven (200°C/180°C fan/400°F/gas mark 6) for 20–25 minutes, depending on how sticky you like your fruit.

22 Monday

'Yesterday, I was clever, so I wanted to change the world.
Today, I am wise, so I am changing myself.' *Rumi*

23 Tuesday

24 Wednesday

25 Thursday

Lemons are my favourite household item. Not only do they
keep my fridge smelling fresh, but the juice, squeezed on apples
or avocados, stops them going brown. They're also brilliant at
refreshing wilted lettuce. Add a couple of teaspoons of lemon juice
into cold water, soak your lettuce in it and it'll perk up no end.

26 Friday

27 Saturday

28 Sunday

Getting Your Home
Autumn-Ready

I like to organise my wardrobe towards the end of August. It's not quite time to put away the summer clothes, but I find that if I get ahead now, I'm not left with a great jumble of warm- and cold-weather outfits clogging up the closet.

I put aside any summer clothing that has been worn or stained (if I can't get the stains out) and decide what is for the charity shop and what is really for recycling. Then I take a look at my autumn–winter clothing to see what is acceptable and what must go! I'm a divil for checking for moths, ever since I had an infestation of them – it took me ages to get rid of them – so now I moth-proof my wardrobe by using cedar balls and lavender spray, and I place my treasured cashmere jumper in a moth-proof bag.

If I'm feeling really organised, I'll schedule a visit from my gas boiler installer. I don't want to find that it's not working in October when I need it! I also poke around in the gutters to make sure there's nothing blocking them – don't do this by yourself! – and I give my chimney sweep a call. I check my carbon monoxide and smoke alarms to see that they're still working and I give my car a once-over to check that I haven't lost the scraper or de-icer since last year. Finally, I bleed the radiators to check for any air bubbles.

29 Monday

30 Tuesday

31 Wednesday

'I'm not superstitious, but I am a little stitious.'
Steve Carell as Mike Scott in The Office

September

1 Thursday

2 Friday

One of my favourite ways to rescue a soft
baguette is to sprinkle it with a little water,
wrap it in tinfoil and pop it in a hot oven for
a few minutes. You'll then have a nice crisp
crust and a soft inside.

3 Saturday

4 Sunday

That Back-to-School Habit

Even though I left school a full fifty years ago now, when September arrives, I have that back-to-school feeling. It's as if a whole new year is beginning, along with the crisp evenings and the creeping darkness. According to scientists, the reason I do this is because the school 'habit' has been hardwired into my brain, meaning that when I pass a stationer's in late August, I'm automatically taken back to my childhood. This revelation got me thinking about habits – the bad ones I'd like to drop and the good ones I'd like to cultivate.

There's a myth that it takes 21 days to form a new habit; scientists now believe that it may take longer. A 2009 study in the European Journal of Social Psychology showed that it takes an average of 66 days to form a new habit. But it can be done! The key is to work on making small changes to your habits, or by changing just one habit at a time.

The other crucial ingredient is, of course, to persist. I knew that I had to give up sugar for health reasons, so I said, 'That's it. No more sugar at all.' Within a couple of days, all I wanted was a piece of cake! So, I focused on gradually eliminating different sugary foods from my diet. I started with sugar in coffee and phased it out over a few weeks, gradually getting used to the taste. Then I moved onto eliminating honey on my toast, and so on. After about six months, I was eating a great deal less sugar – but I had to try and try again, and not beat myself up every time I failed. I hope some of these habit-busters work for you!

5 Monday

'Lots of people want to ride with you in the limo, but what you want is someone who will take the bus with you when the limo breaks down.' *Oprah Winfrey*

6 Tuesday

7 Wednesday

I love to go blackberry picking at this time of year. They are plentiful in the hedgerows near my home, but I have to be quick before everyone else gets them! I wash them thoroughly, soaking them in the sink and skimming off any bugs, before putting them in the freezer.

8 Thursday

9 Friday

Now is the time I give my summer clothes a good wash before putting them away. Apparently, clothes moths love the smell of sweat, so it pays to wash and dry thoroughly.

10 Saturday

11 Sunday

12 Monday

'Autumn is a second spring, when every leaf is a flower.'
Albert Camus

13 Tuesday

14 Wednesday

15 Thursday

When I was a child, we would be sent to pick apples in Granny's garden. We had to separate the ones with bruises (they'd be used for pig feed) from the better ones, and then we had to place layer upon layer of them, with sheets of newspaper in between, into an old blue barrel to keep over the winter. I can still remember that smell of apples when I opened the shed door.

16 Friday

17 Saturday

18 Sunday

The September Equinox

Between 21 and 23 September, the sun hovers over the equator, and both the northern and southern hemispheres get an equal amount of the sun's rays. At this time of year (and at the spring equinox, around 21 March) day and night are of equal length. In the northern hemisphere, we are seeing the signs of autumn, whereas in the southern hemisphere they are just heading into spring.

This time would have had great significance for our ancestors. Cónacht Fómhair was the final Celtic festival of the year, which began again with Samhain, or Hallowe'en. Our ancestors would have seen this time of year as an opportunity to pause and take stock before the shorter days and the colder weather of winter arrived.

In Co. Meath, Sliabh na Caillí, or the Cailleach's Mountain, is actually three mountains, each with a burial chamber on top, where people would have come to worship. The stones in the cairns were believed to have been dropped by a witch as she walked across the country, hence the name. They are thought to be even older than those at Newgrange. At the spring and summer equinox, the sun shines on the back stone of the chamber on the wonderful drawings. But these drawings are more than decoration. Local people have discovered that they are early astronomical drawings, proving that our ancestors were much more sophisticated than we imagined.

19 Monday

'There are years that ask questions and years that answer.'
Zora Neale Hurston

20 Tuesday

21 Wednesday

22 Thursday

23 Friday

24 Saturday

25 Sunday

Apples

I love apples and I eat one every night before bedtime – I find that it keeps my sugar cravings at bay. I love native Irish varieties when I can find them, which sadly isn't that often any more. Historically, the names are so interesting: Bloody Butcher, Lady Fingers of Offaly, Widow's Friend and our own Kerry Pippin, along with Irish Peach, which comes from Co. Sligo, which Mum would have loved.

If you can't find many native varieties of apple, why not try growing your own? The great thing about Irish varieties is that they are grown for our climate and soil type, so they will be easier to grow than other varieties. There are nurseries that sell native trees and the Irish Seed Savers Association can also help: www.irishseedsavers.ie.

When I was looking around for the history of native apples, I came across this entry from an English book called *Mrs Mary Eales's Receipts*, which dates from 1718. I love the quaint language.

To make APPLE-JELLY for all Sorts of SWEET-MEATS.
When the Apples are par'd and quarter'd, put them into the boiling Water; let there be no more Water than just to cover them, and let it boil as fast as possible; when the Apples are all to Pieces, put in about a Quart of Water more; let it boil at least half an Hour; and then run it thro' a Jelly-bag.

26 Monday

'I notice that autumn is more the season of the soul than of nature.'
Friedrich Nietzsche

27 Tuesday

28 Wednesday

29 Thursday

30 Friday

I love planting spring bulbs in September. It reminds me that while winter might be on its way, spring won't be far behind. I like to plant daffodils in a sunny spot, where I know they'll thrive, and I love to put tulip bulbs in dramatic colours into large pots. You can also get started on your wildflower meadow, planting your seeds in a well-drained plot and weeding them regularly. I also move my pelargoniums (tender geraniums) indoors to avoid the first frosts or chills.

October

1 Saturday

2 Sunday

'We can complain because
rose bushes have thorns,
or rejoice because thorn
bushes have roses.'
Abraham Lincoln

The Wild Swans at Coole

This is an extract from a wonderful poem about autumn from Mum's favourite poet, W.B. Yeats.

The trees are in their autumn beauty,
The woodland paths are dry,
Under the October twilight the water
Mirrors a still sky;
Upon the brimming water among the stones
Are nine-and-fifty swans.

The nineteenth autumn has come upon me
Since I first made my count;
I saw, before I had well finished,
All suddenly mount
And scatter wheeling in great broken rings
Upon their clamorous wings.

I have looked upon those brilliant creatures,
And now my heart is sore.
All's changed since I, hearing at twilight,
The first time on this shore,
The bell-beat of their wings above my head,
Trod with a lighter tread.

Unwearied still, lover by lover,
They paddle in the cold
Companionable streams or climb the air;
Their hearts have not grown old;
Passion or conquest, wander where they will,
Attend upon them still.

3 Monday

'Ní bhíonn saoi gan locht.'/'No wise person is without faults.' *Irish proverb*

4 Tuesday

5 Wednesday

When we were children, we would often go up to the reservoir in Bohernabreena to pick hazelnuts, which grew plentifully there. We'd take them home in bags and leave them to dry in the warmth of the kitchen.

6 Thursday

7 Friday

8 Saturday

9 Sunday

10 Monday

11 Tuesday

12 Wednesday

13 Thursday

At this time of year, my mind turns to soup – I find I want something hot at lunchtime now that the days are getting colder. One of my favourites is sweet potato. I peel a big sweet potato, then I sweat an onion on the pan for about ten minutes, adding a minced clove of garlic for the final minute. I add the sweet potato and soften it for about three minutes, then add half a litre of stock and half a can of coconut milk. I let it simmer for about 15 minutes before blitzing it with my hand-held mixer and adding a squeeze of lemon or lime and a small handful of chopped coriander.

14 Friday

15 Saturday

16 Sunday

Light My Fire

In autumn, there's nothing I like better than a roaring fire. I have a log-burner that's easy to light, but the fire in my living-room fireplace is another matter. The other week, as I struggled with fire-lighters and smokeless fuel, growing ever more annoyed and red in the face, it reminded me that a friend of mine asked me to write up some handy tips for lighting a fire.

1. Make sure your chimney is clean. Clean out any old ashes from the fireplace.
2. Warm the chimney or flue. The air will be cold, and if you just light your fire, you'll get a big puff of smoke into the room as the warmth meets the cold air of the chimney. Light a twist of newspaper and stick it up into the chimney or flue. As the hot air rises, the twist will float up and out and the air will be warmed.
3. Twist some more bits of paper and place them at the back of the grate. Add your kindling on top – there doesn't have to be any particular pattern, just leave room for it all to ignite.
4. Now to the log arranging. A hot topic if ever there was one! My sister Kate makes a triangle out of hers on top of the kindling, but I like to place a log vertically at either end of my kindling/paper, then place two logs horizontally on top of them. It works for me.
5. Another method that some swear by is the 'top down' method, i.e. you put the logs at the bottom, the kindling in the middle and the newspaper on top. The newspaper burns down to the kindling and the embers drop down to the logs. Worth a try!

17 Monday

'A river cuts through a rock not because of its power, but because of its persistence.' *James N. Watkins*

18 Tuesday

19 Wednesday

The birds start arriving in my garden around now. They fly about, nosing into flowerbeds and resting on my kitchen windowsill in the hope of being fed. It always surprises me how they just know to return, year after year. This reminds me of a friend of mine who was discussing the little robin who came to see him every year for years. He was only delighted at this show of loyalty, until his friend told him that robins only live for a couple of years!

20 Thursday

21 Friday

22 Saturday

23 Sunday

Look After Yourself

'Self-care' became something of a mantra during the pandemic, and rightly so. It's not just a bit of jargon: it makes sense that if you look after yourself, you'll be better able to look after others and to face life's challenges. But how is the question. Some of us find meditation helpful and it drives others mad; some love a 20-minute bout of vigorous exercise, others – like me! – find themselves red-faced and out of breath. The key is to find what you love doing, what makes you feel good, full of energy and get up and go. I've made a little checklist of my own, which I pin to the fridge weekly to remind myself of what makes me happy. Here are a few ideas to get you started.

- Get a good night's sleep
- Drink eight glasses of water a day
- Watch my favourite TV show
- Take a walk in nature
- Have a 20-minute afternoon snooze
- Eat my favourite meal
- Read a chapter of my latest book
- Listen to music or a documentary on the radio
- Have a nice hot bath
- Ring one of my nieces or nephews for a chat
- Find something that makes me laugh out loud
- Do my good deed for the day

Your list might not look like mine, but the idea is to pick things that you want to do and not what you should do – there's another list for that!

24 Monday

'There are two ways of spreading light: to be the candle or the mirror that reflects it.' *Edith Wharton*

25 Tuesday

I met a girl in the supermarket the other day. She was holding two tubs; one was baking powder and the other was baking soda. She didn't know which was which! Not unusual. Both are 'leaveners', i.e. they help things to rise, but baking soda needs an acid like buttermilk or lemon juice to help it, a chemical reaction if you like; baking powder is bicarb plus cream of tartar and simply needs liquid, so you can leave your biscuits or cake around for longer. Always follow the recipe if you want to get it right. Mind you, she wanted it for an art project, so I had no idea which one to suggest to her!

26 Wednesday

27 Thursday

28 Friday

29 Saturday

The clocks go back tonight. You'll get an extra hour in bed, but it'll get dark earlier after today, so make sure that you get out in the morning if you can, when the light is best. You'll really notice the difference.

30 Sunday

'The love of gardening
is a seed once sown that
never dies but grows to the
enduring happiness that
the love of gardening gives.'
Gertrude Jekyll

Báirín Breac

I love Hallowe'en and my favourite cake of all is the barmbrack, full of rich fruit, in a light, spicy dough. It's delicious spread with butter and eaten with a nice cup of tea.

Ingredients

350g mixed dried fruit
250ml cold black tea (1 mug)
30ml whiskey (optional)
225g self-raising flour

125g brown sugar
1 tsp mixed spice
1 egg, beaten

Method

1. The evening before you plan to make the cake, place the fruit mix in a bowl and cover with the cold tea and whiskey, if using. Leave to plump up overnight.
2. Grease and line a 2lb loaf tin. Heat the oven to 170°C/150°C fan/325°F/gas mark 3.
3. Place the dry ingredients in a mixing bowl and whisk to mix.
4. Add the beaten egg and stir gently, then gradually pour in the tea from the bowl of dried fruit until you have a sticky dough.
5. Add the fruit and stir gently to combine.
6. Pour into the loaf tin, place in the middle of your oven and bake for an hour. If the top looks as if it's burning, place a piece of foil loosely over the top. Check to see if the cake is done by inserting a skewer into the middle. If it comes out clean, the cake is done.
7. Let the cake cool a little on a wire rack before turning it out gently and leaving it to cool completely.

31 Monday OCTOBER BANK HOLIDAY

'There is something at work in my soul, which I do not understand.' *Mary Shelley*, Frankenstein

November

1 Tuesday ALL SAINTS' DAY

2 Wednesday ALL SOULS' DAY

I love the superstitions associated with this time of the year. On All Souls' night, the dead would come back to visit and candles would be lit on every windowsill to guide them home. Bonfires would be lit at Hallowe'en to keep bad luck at bay and the ashes would be spread on the fields the next day to bring a good harvest.

3 Thursday

4 Friday

If I run out of my favourite cleaning spray, I pop a couple of drops of washing-up liquid into a spray bottle and use that instead. It's an excellent cleaner, and not as harsh as many modern sprays.

5 Saturday

6 Sunday

Cold, Clear and Blue

This untitled poem by Emily Brontë sums up the beauty and harshness of winter for me.

Cold, clear, and blue the morning heaven
Expands its arch on high;
Cold, clear, and blue Lake Werna's water
Reflects that winter sky:
The moon has set, but Venus shines,
A silent, silvery star.

Will the day be bright or cloudy?
Sweetly has its dawn begun;
But the heaven may shake with thunder
Ere the settling sun.

Lady, watch Apollo's journey;
Thus thy first hour's course shall be;
If his beams through summer vapours
Warm the earth all placidly,
Her days shall pass like a pleasant dream in sweet
tranquillity.

If it darken, if a shadow
Quench his rays and summon rain,
Flowers may open, buds may blossom,
Bud and flower alike are vain;
Her days shall pass like a mournful story in care and
tears and pain.

7 Monday

'One kind word can warm three winter months.'
Japanese proverb

8 Tuesday

9 Wednesday

I'm trying to get ahead for Christmas this year by buying presents when I see them and putting them away, instead of spending a frantic week before the big day buying random things. I also order online, but I try to focus on lovely Irish crafts and gifts, if possible.

10 Thursday

11 Friday

12 Saturday

13 Sunday

14 Monday

Some of us wilt a little in winter, due to the lack of sunlight. Try to get out in the morning, when the sun is brightest; if you get really blue, a light box might help. These LED screens replicate sunlight and you can place them beside your workspace or at the kitchen table to give you a little boost. They are available in all kinds of shapes and sizes, but 2,500 lux is what you need as a minimum.

15 Tuesday

16 Wednesday

17 Thursday

18 Friday

19 Saturday

20 Sunday

Traditionally, this was the day when you made your Christmas pudding, but I'm sure Mum made hers even earlier than this. Not only that, but she would make a Christmas cake for ourselves and our neighbours, and she would 'feed' it with brandy or whiskey every day until Christmas. Boozy doesn't even cover it …

Decluttering for Christmas

Even though the Christmas preparations are in full swing at the Park Hotel Kenmare, I still like to use any opportunity I can to get my own house Christmas-ready.

- A friend of mine gets her children to sort through their toy boxes at this time of year and remove anything they don't want. The theory is that there'll be room for all the new toys!
- I try to get my stock of picture books down to a manageable level. People often give them to me as gifts and I love them, but every now and then I'll whittle them down and bring them to the local book bank, along with a few novels.
- I remove the washable covers from my sofa and give them a wash at a low temperature. It's not that they get dirty as such, it's just to freshen them up.
- I hunt around in the hot press for my linen tablecloth and matching napkins, to bring to the launderette in good time for Christmas. A friend of mine worked in a launderette as a student and it used to amuse her how many people turned up in November looking for the tablecloth they'd left in to be laundered the previous January – they'd forgotten all about it!
- Candles are something I often forget, so I look in the drawers to check that I have nice full ones and not little wax stumps.
- Finally, I give the rooms a good hoover, wipe off all the dust with a microfibre cloth, and I polish the dining room table with beeswax. All done!

21 Monday

'Life is like a ten-speed bicycle. Most of us have gears we never use.' *Charles M. Schultz*

22 Tuesday

23 Wednesday

Time to go up to the attic to check on my store of Christmas lights. I always find that at least one string isn't working, so I take them down and plug them in to check. Then I drape them on the windowsill and admire the lovely colours that add such brightness to the dark November evenings.

24 Thursday

25 Friday

26 Saturday

27 Sunday ADVENT SUNDAY

Today marks the beginning of the four-week religious preparations for Christmas.

Christmas Traditions from Around the World

In Japan, people head out for Kentucky Fried Chicken on Christmas Day. Apparently, the tradition started as a marketing wheeze, but then caught on, and people queue for ages or order their KFC buckets well in advance!

It's interesting how many Christmas traditions involve the devil or evil spirits. In Norway, people hide brooms and sweeping brushes before they go to bed on Christmas Eve, so that the many witches and ghosts believed to wander about at night can't find them. In Italy, La Befana, or the witch, helps Santa Claus to deliver presents on 5 January and in Austria, men dress up in devil costumes and wander the streets to carry away anyone who has been naughty – children fear that this creature, known as Krampus, might bring them something unpleasant for Christmas, instead of a gift.

In Ukraine, Christmas is celebrated on 7 January by dressing up and eating a traditional porridge-like dish mixed with nuts and honey, and Christmas trees are dressed with cobwebs, in homage to an old folk tale. In Finland, rice pudding is eaten on Christmas morning; and in Barbados, a nice baked ham. However, my favourite Christmas tradition comes from Caracas in Venezuela, where there is a tradition of rollerskating to Mass on Christmas morning!

28 Monday

'Family is not an important thing. It is everything.' *Michael J. Fox*

29 Tuesday

30 Wednesday

December

1 Thursday

I don't know about you, but as I get older, I find that I don't want or need anything much. My nieces and nephews always buy me a present, and I buy presents for them, but otherwise, we do Kris Kindle, so all I have to buy is one present. I know, I sound like Scrooge, but less really is more these days!

2 Friday

3 Saturday

4 Sunday

How to Have a Sustainable Christmas

Trying to be a bit more eco-friendly is high on my list of priorities and as Christmas can often be a time of waste, it's a great opportunity to try to do things more sustainably.

- Shop local. As we learned during the pandemic, our support can help local businesses to survive and thrive.
- Buy one good gift instead of lots of little ones. It's less wasteful and I can buy something nicer for each person on my list.
- Try alternative wrapping for your gifts this year. You can try furoshiki, which is the Japanese art of wrapping gifts in fabric – endlessly recyclable and pretty too.
- I spotted reusable crackers in a shop this year and bought six of them. They can be recycled and you can put your own – nice – gifts in them as well. We had a French chef at the hotel once, Hervé, who was pleasant, if not possessed of a brilliant sense of humour. Now, we always have a staff dinner on Christmas Day and along came Hervé, with his wife and three-month-old baby. I used to buy the best crackers I could and when we all sat down, I offered one to our head receptionist, Jenny, to pull. She did so with gusto and it gave a loud bang, as they do, whereupon the baby started roaring. Hervé promptly got up and went around the table, removing the bangs from all the crackers! Jenny couldn't contain herself. Now, at every staff Christmas dinner, she'll remind me of Hervé and the bangless crackers.

5 Monday   'Tension is who you think you should be. Relaxation is who you are.' *Chinese proverb*

6 Tuesday

7 Wednesday   A friend of mine adored Christmas pudding and used to make several every year. One year, she got the idea of making a couple of mini puddings in these little enclosed 'cocottes' which are used to bake eggs. She put the puddings in the cocottes and into boiling water to steam, and went off to watch the news. After half an hour, there was an almighty bang, and when she came into the kitchen, she found that the cocottes had exploded and the ceiling was plastered with Christmas pudding!

8 Thursday

9 Friday

10 Saturday

11 Sunday

12 Monday

13 Tuesday

14 Wednesday

Parents want to give their children a magical Christmas, but try not to worry if Christmas World or the ice-skating is fully booked. These jaunts can be very expensive and busy, too. One of my nephews liked nothing better than to examine the elaborate Lego arrangements in Arnott's shop window – he would spend hours there. A friend of mine splashed out on tickets to the pantomime in the Gaiety and her five-year-old was so terrified at the noise and colour that she had to take him home early! Simple things are often less stressful with children, I'm told.

15 Thursday

16 Friday

17 Saturday

18 Sunday

Christmas Dinner Ideas for Special Diets

Nowadays, you're quite likely to invite a vegetarian, pescatarian or vegan to Christmas dinner, so you'll need to have something handy for them.

Fish is ideal for pescatarians. I buy fresh tuna for one of my nephews, and quickly sear it on a pan at the last minute, while the turkey is resting. It only takes a couple of minutes. Baking fish like salmon or cod in foil is also a great way to cook fish, because it won't dry out.

You don't *have* to serve a nut roast to vegetarians! But, mind you, it is tasty and goes very well with the vegetables. First, line a loaf tin with baking paper, then make what the Italians call a 'soffritto', which is a mix of an onion, a carrot and a celery stick, chopped finely and sautéed gently on the pan. To this, you add your spices: some cumin – I love its warming flavour – and a teaspoon of dried mixed herbs. Then add a tin of crushed tomatoes and your veg – I like cooked lentils for bulk and because they hold up well in the loaf shape. You can cook 200g of lentils for 20 minutes at a simmer or – whisper it – buy a handy pack of ready-cooked Puy lentils, which are brilliant. And don't forget the nuts! About 200g of chopped nuts, stirred in well, will be perfect, and perhaps add 50g of dried fruit for sweetness – I like the tartness of cranberries. Press gently into your loaf tin and bake for 45 minutes or so at 180°C/160°C fan/350°F/gas mark 4. If you have any questions about nut roasts, the Vegetarian Society has some great versions: https://vegsoc.org/recipes.

19 Monday

'There is nothing in the world so irresistibly contagious as laughter and good humour.' *Charles Dickens*, A Christmas Carol

20 Tuesday

21 Wednesday

22 Thursday

23 Friday

24 Saturday

I like to boil the ham on Christmas Eve and prepare it for the oven the following day. Nigella Lawson swears by Coca-Cola as a glaze! She might well be right, but I prefer the classic glaze of butter and brown sugar, studded with cloves. I also prepare the veg for roasting, peeling and slicing potatoes, carrots and parsnips. Then I nag Kate to make sure she's remembered the starter and remind Susan about dessert.

25 Sunday CHRISTMAS DAY

'I will honour Christmas in my heart, and try to keep it all the year.'
Charles Dickens,
A Christmas Carol

Making the Most of Down Time

I say this with a slight sense of irony because we don't get any at the hotel! But for those of you lucky enough to have the holiday off, try to relax and enjoy it. It's the one time of the year when there really is nothing much else to do but to watch a good film or read a book. I always buy myself a non-fiction book for Christmas reading, because I can read sections of it during my free time, while a novel requires more continuity.

I also like to bake simple gingerbread cookies or a cake. I found that one online retailer was selling 'Ugly Sweater Christmas Cookies' – how could I resist! Ginger cake is one of my favourites and it fills the kitchen with that lovely Christmassy scent. And, because I'm not a drinker, I've become very good at making non-alcoholic drinks like gingerbread lattes (warm milk heated gently with spices like cinnamon and nutmeg, a little dash of black coffee, and a dollop of cream) or a 'champagne' cocktail using sugar syrup topped with fizzy water.

You could also be like Sir Paul McCartney, who has a Christmas playlist for his family. If you don't like the classic compilations, try making one of your own (or get a young person to do it!). Then you can have all the songs you love.

If I have time, I like to spend it outdoors, taking a brisk winter walk. It may be chilly, but it always perks me up. I love to see the fields covered in frost and the river meandering through the countryside.

26 Monday ST STEPHEN'S DAY

'No river can return to its source, yet all rivers must have a beginning.'
Native American proverb

27 Tuesday

28 Wednesday

29 Thursday

30 Friday

31 Saturday NEW YEAR'S EVE

Time to look forward to a New Year and new beginnings, whatever they might be.
Athbhlian faoi mhaise!

January

1 Sunday NEW YEAR'S DAY

'If at first you don't succeed, then skydiving definitely isn't for you.'
Steven Wright

ESSENTIAL CONTACTS

Name	
Address	
Mobile	
Email	

Name	
Address	
Mobile	
Email	

Name	
Address	
Mobile	
Email	

Name	
Address	
Mobile	
Email	

Name	
Address	
Mobile	
Email	

Name	
Address	
Mobile	
Email	

Name	
Address	
Mobile	
Email	

Name	
Address	
Mobile	
Email	

Name	
Address	
Mobile	
Email	

Name	
Address	
Mobile	
Email	

Name	
Address	
Mobile	
Email	

Name	
Address	
Mobile	
Email	

Name	
Address	
Mobile	
Email	

Name	
Address	
Mobile	
Email	

Name	
Address	
Mobile	
Email	

Name	
Address	
Mobile	
Email	

Name	
Address	
Mobile	
Email	

Name	
Address	
Mobile	
Email	

Name	
Address	
Mobile	
Email	

Name	
Address	
Mobile	
Email	

Name	
Address	
Mobile	
Email	

Name	
Address	
Mobile	
Email	

Name	
Address	
Mobile	
Email	

Name	
Address	
Mobile	
Email	

Name	
Address	
Mobile	
Email	

Name	
Address	
Mobile	
Email	

Name	
Address	
Mobile	
Email	

Name	
Address	
Mobile	
Email	

Name	
Address	
Mobile	
Email	

Name	
Address	
Mobile	
Email	

NOTES